M000107520

THE MEDICAL I CHING

ORACLE OF THE HEALER WITHIN

MIKI SHIMA

Foreword By
Grandmaster Sango Kobayashi

Published by:

Blue Poppy Press
1775 Linden Ave. Boulder, CO 80304
(303) 447-8372

First Edition October, 1992
Second Printing, October 1997

ISBN 0-936185-38-4
Library of Congress #92-73393

Copyright © Miki Shima

All rights reserved. No part of this book may be reproduced, stored in a retrieval system, or transcribed in any form, by any means electronic, mechanical, photocopy, recording, or other means, or translated into any other language without prior written permission of the publisher.

The information in this book is given in good faith. However, the translators and the publishers cannot be held responsible for any error or omission. Nor can they be held in any way responsible for treatment given on the basis of information contained in this book. The publishers make this information available to English readers for scholarly and research purposes only.

The publishers do not advocate nor endorse self-medication by laypersons. Chinese medicine is a professional medicine. Laypersons interested in availing themselves of the treatments described in this book should seek out a qualified professional practitioner of Chinese medicine.

COMP Designation: Original work

Printed at Johnson Books
Calligraphy by Miki Shima. Cover design by Anne Rue.

10, 9, 8, 7, 6, 5, 4, 3, 2

Dedicated to

Grand Master Sango Kobayashi, Ph.D.,
My wife Diana,
All my children, Laura, Jeremy, and Kenny,
Who have all loved and helped me so much

Acknowledgments

Most of the material in this book is based on workshops on the *I Ching* and related subjects that I have taught over the past ten years. Thanks, therefore, are due the many students who attended these workshops and whose questions helped me clarify this material all the more. I am also greatly honored to have Dr. Sango Kobayashi as my personal mentor in the *I Ching* and I owe him a great deal for his generous instruction.

I would also like to thank Dr. Jay Sordean who helped me very much for many years as program director of the Japanese-American Acupuncture Foundation (JAAF), Inc. All my friends from the California Acupuncture Association also assisted me greatly in keeping my spirit up during the process of writing this book.

Finally, I am very grateful for the considerate encouragement and intelligent advice I received from Bob Flaws and Honora Lee Wolfe in preparing this book for publication. Without their friendly support, this book could not have manifested the way it is.

Notes on This Edition

Except for the title of the *I Ching*, Chinese words used in this edition have first been given in *pinyin* romanization followed in parentheses by the Wade-Giles system. Hopefully, this will make this book more easily usable to practitioners of Traditional Chinese Medicine who are familiar with *pinyin* romanization and *I Ching* readers and users who are typically more familiar with the Wade-Giles system. We have chosen to simply use the Wade-Giles *I Ching* in the title of this book since that is its most recognizable form to the majority of this book's potential readers.

Although this book may be used by practitioners of any and all healing arts, since it stems from the Chinese tradition, much of the medical terminology is couched in the language of Traditional Chinese Medicine. Readers unfamiliar with the basic theories and tenets of Chinese medicine should see Ted Kaptchuk's *The Web That Has No Weaver* published by Congdon & Weed.

Foreword

The *I Ching* is the essence of Chinese philosophy. Conceived some 6,000 years ago by Fu Xi, a legendary sage, it is the *magnum opus* of Oriental metaphysics. Without the principles of yin and yang of the *I Ching*, one cannot even envisage Oriental philosophy.

Besides being the preeminent book of Chinese philosophy and wisdom, it is also a book of divination based on a superb system of binary representations of patterns in the universe completed by King Wen of the Zhou Dynasty. Accepted as the most reliable method of prognostication, the *I Ching* has been used by tens of thousands of people in the Orient as an oracular method regarding every conceivable subject in human life. Now, it has been transplanted in the West and has begun producing some significant results.

The author of the present work, Dr. Miki Shima, has not only studied the *I Ching* in depth but has also practiced it profoundly for the past 25 years. The thing that so impresses me about Dr. Shima is that he has been tirelessly casting the *I Ching* every day and that he has gathered an immense amount of practical knowledge on the art of divination from his direct experience. I know a great many people who study the *I Ching*, but I have never met anyone who practices this divination like Dr. Shima. This is what makes him different from traditional *I Ching* scholars. I know for a fact that he has kept very good records of his divination and that he studies them over and over again for long periods of time. The present work is, therefore, derived not only from his academic endeavor on the subject of the *I Ching* but also directly from his personal knowledge and experience.

Since Dr. Shima began his career as a practitioner of Oriental medicine more than 20 years ago, he has become a master of using the *I Ching* in the medical field. He is extremely good at diagnosing and detecting deep etiologies. He is also superb with prognostication and treatment protocols. Thus, he has become a great physician by using the information obtained from his practice of the *I Ching*.

I firmly believe that the present volume is the first of this kind in the West and will further the understanding of this ancient book of wisdom. I have no hesitation in recommending Dr. Shima's work on the *I Ching* to anyone interested in practicing medicine whether it be Western or Oriental.

Sango Kobayashi, Ph.D.
President
Tokyo *I Ching* College
Kanto College of Oriental Medicine

May, 1992
Tokyo, Japan

Preface

In China, the *I Ching* or *Classic of Change* has been revered as *the* most profound book of wisdom for millenia. It is both a book of philosophy to be studied and contemplated and a manual of divination. In the Orient, this book has fascinated countless scholars and philosophers so much that they have studied and consulted it on every conceivable problem in life. Because of the different interests and proclivities of its different users, now there exist even in English a number of specialized versions of the *I Ching*. There is a Confucian *I Ching*, a Daoist *I Ching*, a Buddhist *I Ching*, a diviner's *I Ching*, etc. Since health and wellbeing are an intrinsic concern of all human beings, it is reasonable to assume that individuals have been consulting the *I Ching* for millenia on medical matters as well. However, till now, no book on the medical use of the *I Ching* has been available in English.

I have been studying classical Chinese literature for the past thirty years, having completed my Master's degree in linguistics at the University of Michigan, and nothing has excited me more than the *I Ching*. I was first "accidentally" introduced to the *I Ching* by a high school history teacher. I started using the *I Ching* for divination under this teacher's guidance and have never since quit. In 1984, I met Grandmaster Sango Kobayashi in Tokyo. Dr. Kobayashi, besides being a practitioner of Chinese medicine, is author of some fifty books on the *I Ching*. Since 1984, I have been consulting Dr. Kobayashi in my personal study and use of this preeminent classic.

In particular, for the last two decades, I have been greatly using the *I Ching* in my practice of acupuncture and Chinese medicine. Although the *I Ching* was not a part of my traditional medical training, I began incorporating its use into my study and practice immediately after I became interested in Chinese medicine. As a neophyte, I was desperately trying to gain insight into my patients' conditions and the *I Ching* immediately presented itself as a special source of information and guidance. Although it may sound odd to those who know little or nothing about the *I Ching*, this book has provided me with a great deal of medical information and I have been able to help many of my patients due to proper decisions based on its counsel.

As I became more and more involved in the medical use of the *I Ching*, I began to need more advanced knowledge in this field. To my great chagrin, I had to search very hard for information on this particular use of the *I Ching* because there are only a few small compendia of medical information by past *I Ching* masters. I had to read a great many books on the subject to find only bits and pieces of incoherent information. It literally took me years to get even a fuzzy picture of the art of medical divination. Now I am convinced that, without a good knowledge of the *I Ching*, there is no understanding of Chinese medicine, since it embodies the very essence of Chinese medicine in the purest manner. This is because the theory, diagnosis, and practice of Chinese medicine are all firmly based on yin yang theory and the *I Ching* is the classical fountainhead of yin yang philosophy and symbolism. Without going back to this origin of the symbols and metaphors of the ancient Chinese tradition, one cannot fully understand and appreciate the height and depth of the immense body of Chinese medical wisdom.

The object of the present volume is to explain how the *I Ching* can be used as a guide in the practice of Chinese medicine and the healing arts in general. It is a compilation of what I have gathered over the past two decades through my practice of divination and my research of the Chinese and Japanese *I Ching* literature. It is neither intended to be an exhaustive academic work nor a handbook on *I Ching* divination in general. Rather, it specifically explains how to use the *I Ching* as a diagnostic and and prognosticative tool in medical practice. For those interested in more general and historical information about the *I Ching*, I recommend Richard Wilhelm's *The I Ching or Book of Changes*. I have also included the names of other English language *I Ching* sources in the bibliography.

Just as there is no end to the study of Chinese medicine, so likewise there is no end to the study of the *I Ching*. It has taken me twenty years to read all the basic books on the *I Ching* in Chinese and Japanese. Therefore, take your time and enjoy. The *I Ching* will help you throughout your life.

Contents

3

Casting the *I Ching* 27

4

Interpreting the *I Ching* 51

5

Medical Readings for the 64 Hexagrams 63

6

Classical *I Ching* Case Histories 191

1

The Rationale for Using the *I Ching* in Medical Practice

According to Chinese tradition, the building blocks of the *I Ching* as a philosophical and divinatory system were laid by Fu Xi, the most ancient Chinese culture hero in 3,322 BC. At that time, it is believed that the eight *gua* or trigrams, the eight building blocks of the 64 hexagrams which form the core of the *I Ching*, were revealed to Fu Xi on the back of a turtle. Around 1143 BC, it is believed that King Wen of the Zhou Dynasty wrote the commentaries on these 64 hexagrams. Several years later, the Duke of Zhou, regent to King Cheng, wrote the commentaries on the so-called changing lines. And around, 500 BC, Confucius, during his later years, wrote the so-called Ten Wings which are a further series of commentaries on the images, judgements, order of arrangement, and other aspects of what even by Confucius' time was regarded as a hoary and venerable classic.

Traditionally, there have been two schools of *I Ching* students. One school is composed of those who merely study and analyze the *I Ching* academically and philosophically. Members of this group do not deign to use this book as a divinatory tool and typically look down on such users as ignorant and credulous fortune-tellers. The other school is composed of those who tend not to care about the technical fine points of this book's philological or historical analysis but who use this book as a daily guide to the living of life. Although it is my experience that the more one understands about the inner workings and arrangement of the *I Ching* theoretically and philosophically the more profound a guide it becomes, those of its students who do not use this book as a tool for living remind me of scholars who study Zen but who never sit in meditation. Unless one experiences it directly, one cannot know Zen. In the same way, unless one puts the wisdom contained in this book into practice in their daily life, one can hardly appreciate the profundity of its counsel.

Nonetheless, as far as the fundamental mechanism of *I Ching* divination is concerned, I have never yet found a thoroughly convincing theory, be it mathematical, psychological, or philosophical. The workings of the *I Ching* seem to be beyond the understanding of the rational mind. Suffice it to say that its use as a divinatory tool is based on the concepts of synchronicity and what is called in Chinese *ying*. *Ying* means resonance. Those who use the *I Ching* for prognostication and guidance recognize that everything in the phenomenal universe is all of a single piece and that two events that occur simultaneously in time are manifestations of a single *zeitgeist* or pattern of manifestation in the universe at that point in time. Things that happen at the same time are coincidental but not randomly or accidentally so.

The name of this book, the *I Ching*, helps explain how and why this book can help one in any endeavor, including medical practice. The word *ching (jing)* means classic. It is applied to any of a group of hoary Chinese books which are particularly revered for the wisdom they contain. The word *i (yi)*, on the other hand, means change. Its Chinese ideogram is made up of pictures of the sun and moon. The authors of this book knew that the world of phenomena is a world of ceaseless flux or change. Everything is constantly changing, evolving and devolving, being born, growing, reaching maturity, decaying, and dying. However, within this constant flux and movement, the world seems to change in an orderly or rhythmic fashion. Certain patterns can be discerned in the progression of a day and night, the life of a plant, animal, or human, the progression of the seasons, and the natural history of any thing apprehendable by the human mind. By casting the *I Ching*, one is presented with a symbolic picture or image of the pattern of change operative at that point in time. Thus at least some inklings of the workings of the world may be discerned.

The practice of traditional Chinese medicine is based on the recognition of patterns of change within one's patients. When these patterns of change or *zheng* are harmonious and foster life and well being, we say the patient is healthy or recuperating. But when these patterns of change are disharmonious or tend to foster death and dissolution of the body and mind, we say the patient is ill and seek to remedy their disease with appropriate therapies and medications. Such therapies and medications do nothing more or less than nudge the patient's pattern of change from a disharmonious and life-negating trend to a harmonious and life-promoting course.

Further, Chinese medicine recognizes that the qi or life functions of the individual are not distinct from the qi or functions of the macrocosmic whole. In Chinese medicine, one can speak of the person's individual qi as being the guest or *ke qi* within the ruling, host, or *zhu qi* of the universe. Chinese medicine, as does Chinese philosophy in general, believes that a person is truly healthy only when their own internal or guest qi is in harmonious balance and accord with the ruling host qi. Therefore, it is easy to see that anything that might help a physician understand the patterns of change at work in the world might also help them fathom the disease mechanisms at work within their patients. Casting the *I Ching* is just one very ancient and authentic way of understanding the patterns of the universe as they relate to human beings at a particular time and place. Sifu Tsuei Wei of Oakland has said,

> "If the *Nei Jing* is the door to the treasure-house of Chinese medical classics, then the *I Ching* is its key."[1]

Sun Si-miao, the great Tang Dynasty master of medicine has said,

> "If you do not study the *I Ching*, you cannot understand medicine at all."[2]

---

[1]   Tsuei Wei, *Roots of Chinese Culture & Medicine*, Chinese Culture Books Co., Oakland, CA, 1989, p. 21

[2]   Chao Chen, "Yi and Medicine", *Studies on the Application of the Book of Changes*, Vol. 2, Chung Hua Books Co, Ltd., Taipei, 1982, p. 439

Chinese medicine, it is said, is easy to study but difficult to master. It is not so much a science in the Western sense as an art. Chinese doctors hone their sensibilities, their mastery of the theories of Chinese medicine, and their ability to think rationally with these theories over their entire lifetimes. Yet health and disease, as parts of life, are vast and complex and often defy logic and rationality. Textbook descriptions of diagnosis may appear simple and clear-cut on paper, but real-life patients rarely present in such clear-cut, simple ways. There is always so much that we as physicians do not know about our patients compared to what we do know based on our limited perceptions and logic. Often, this discrepancy between what we know about our patients and what we need to know in order to treat them wisely and well is extremely frustrating.

By casting the *I Ching*, the physician, be they Chinese doctor or practitioner of any other healing art, can access a deeper level of knowledge. This level is not necessarily rational. In fact, it would be better to call it an intuitive level of knowledge. The images and symbols which the *I Ching* present to the medical diviner can help the practitioner see their cases from a different perspective. They can jog the physician's memory or suggest the relevance of one piece of information over a welter of conflicting bits of data. They can suggest alternative ways of seeing one's patients and, thus, alternative ways of treating stubborn or recalcitrant cases. They can help us identify the root causes of our patients' disease so that we can cut to the core and not become lost treating superficial symptoms. And these same images and symbols can help us understand the prognosis or probable outcome of the case at hand and answer such questions as whether to take on the patient or not, will they respond to therapy as expected, are there hidden dangers in the case, will their disease progress or regress slowly or quickly, etc.

Essentially, the *I Ching* identifies patterns of qi at work within the world. These patterns are not static but are movements within a ceaseless change and these movements of change tend to develop according to consistent patterns. However, these patterns, like life itself, are not easily reduced to the linear descriptions favored by Western logic and the rational mind. The *I Ching*'s descriptions of these patterns are couched in a highly symbolic, allusive, and

4

evocative language. Modern Westerners are used to thinking in a linear and diachronic way, but the language of the *I Ching* is symbolic and synchronic. We tend to think of time and space in a linear way as if things happen as a chain of cause and effect phenomena. But this is not the world the *I Ching* describes. The world of the *I Ching* is more like a web of numerous patterns which are organically and synchronically intertwined without clear-cut cause and effect relationships. This is the world of interdependent arisings.

When studying and casting the *I Ching* for medical purposes, it is, therefore, important to understand that the images the *I Ching* presents are merely symbolical expressions of medical conditions open to a wide range of possible interpretations. As such, there is no infallible right or correct interpretation of an *I Ching* reading. Rather the *I Ching* presents a pattern which we are free to interpret depending upon the needs of the situation at hand and our own intuition. The fact that the *I Ching* is not entirely rational is exactly the point in that it helps the practitioner access, value, and take into account nonrational, nonlinear elements of reality when approaching their patient.

2

The Basic Building Blocks & Ideas of the *I Ching* and Their Use in Medical Divination

Yin and Yang

Although the vision of the phenomenal world of the *I Ching* is one of ceaseless change, it is yin yang philosophy which explains the dynamic behind the perpetual motion of the phenomenal world. According to the philosopher Zhu Xi (1130-1200 AD), one of the greatest systematic thinkers China ever created and a great authority on the *I Ching*, the phenomenal world is created by *tai ji (tai chi)* or the great ultimate which arises spontaneously from *wu ji (wu chi)* or ultimate nothingness. This *tai ji* is omnipresent, omnipotent, and omniscient and precedes both time and space. This great ultimate created/creates the universe or phenomenal world through the interactions of yin and yang. These are the *liang yi (liang i)* or two modes. Thus yin and yang are the two great primordial forces of nature.

As Zhu Xi states:

> Everything is composed of yin and yang. There is nothing which is not composed of yin and yang...Among humans, there are man and woman. In terms of the body, yin and yang each also pertain to the blood and qi. The blood is yin and the qi is yang.[1]

From this, yin and yang are understood as two oppositional poles of a dichotomy. This is the first point to know about yin and yang.

---

[1]   Zhu Xi, *Zhu Xi Yu Lei (The Collected Teachings of Zhu Xi)*, edited by Keiji Yamada, Ph.D., Iwanami Publishing, 1978, Tokyo, p. 204

Diagram showing the progression from *tai ji* to yin & yang to the *si xiang*, four manifestations, and thence to the eight trigrams or *ba gua*.

(From Zhang Jing-yue's *Lei Jing Tung Yi*
[*The Systematic Classic's Illustrated Appendix*])

At the same time, yin and yang also need to be understood as alternating and complementary forces. In other words, yin constantly changes into yang and yang constantly changes into yin. Thus they complement each other while at the same time their alternation is the seamless flux of change and process. Zhu Xi states:

> Yin and yang can be said to be opposite to each other, like husband and wife, man and woman, east and west, north and south. At the same time, they also have alternating and complementary qualities, like day and night, spring and summer, autumn and winter.[2]

This is the second thing to know about yin and yang.

The third thing is that yin and yang form a constant cycle of regeneration and degeneration. Zhu Xi says:

> Yin and yang are nothing but the manifestation of qi. When yin qi degenerates, yang qi regenerates, and when yang qi degenerates, yin qi regenerates.[3]

Thus in traditional Chinese thinking, the universe or *dao (t'ao)* is only created and properly maintained by this constant cycle of opposition and alternation of yin and yang. The *I Ching*, which is the most fundamental expression of yin yang philosophy, also states:

> The changes of yin and yang contain the measure of heaven and earth. Therefore, they enable us to know the *dao* of heaven and earth and its order.[4]

---

[2]   Ibid., p. 401

[3]   Ibid., p. 400

[4]   Shang Bing-he, *Zhou Yi Shang Shi Xue (Master Shang's Study of the Zhou Yi)*, China Publishing House, Beijing, 1979, p. 290

Thus in describing the patterns of change in the phenomenal world, the authors of the *I Ching* start with yin and yang. Change is the process of yin transforming into yang and yang transforming into yin. Based on this, all patterns of change are nothing other than more and more complex combinations of yin and yang in the process of transformation. In the *I Ching*, yin is symbolized as a broken line and yang by a solid line.

Like the *I Ching*, Chinese medicine is also fundamentally based on yin yang philosophy. Many other principles in Chinese medicine, for instance, the eight principles of pattern diagnosis, the arrangement of the 28 pulses, and Zhang Zhong-jing's six phases are all based on yin yang theory. In fact, without yin and yang, there is no Chinese medicine. The *Nei Jing*, the premier classic of Chinese medicine, itself states:

> Yin and yang are the *dao* of heaven and earth. They are the principles
> of the myriad matters of the universe and the father and mother of
> change.[5]

Because both the *I Ching* and Chinese medicine are based on yin yang philosophy, it is especially appropriate to relate these two together and it is no wonder that the *I Ching* so aptly lends itself to symbolizing the concepts of Chinese medicine. Both are built upon the same binary vision and description of reality.

---

[5]   *Huang Di Nei Jing Su Wen (Emperor Huang's Internal Classic : Simple Questions)*, Vol. 2, Chapter 5, Department of Commerce Publishing House, Beijing, 1954, p. 27

The Eight Trigrams

As symbols, one broken line and one solid line can only express the fundamental dichotomy and complementarity of yin and yang. However, the world is made up of an almost endless variety of things or, we could say, infinite combinations of yin and yang. In order to symbolize more complex combinations of yin and yang, combinations of solid and broken lines were created. Although in terms of Chinese yin yang philosophy there are four possible combinations of yin and yang lines as shown below and called the *si xiang* or four forms, for some reason, the ancient Chinese chose the eight possible combinations of three solid and broken lines now known as the *ba gua (ba k'ua)* or eight trigrams as the building blocks of the *I Ching* system of divination.

It is these eight three line symbols which Fu Xi is supposed to have seen on the back of a turtle. Each of these *gua* symbolize a more complicated combination of yin and yang than either only a single broken and solid line or two broken and/or solid lines. These eight trigrams are shown below.

The eight trigrams came to be associated with various aspects and elements of the phenomenal world, all of which are somehow perceived to resonate together due to their same proportions of yin and yang. Thus, the eight primary trigrams of the *I Ching* are traditionally called by specific names with distinctive symbolic connotations, correspondences, or resonances. Their names and correspondences, including medical correspondences, are as follows:

11

1. *Qian (Ch'ien)*, the Creative, Heaven

——————————— This trigram consists of three yang or solid lines and
——————————— symbolizes the creative or heaven. This is the most yang in
——————————— nature among all eight trigrams and is traditionally symbolized
by the dragon. It also signifies creativity, originality, ingenuity, strength, force,
power, abundance, affluence, opulence, prosperity, aggressiveness, hostility,
vivacity, vitality, health, protection, control, domination, authority, action,
movement, vastness, leaders, kings, gold, the father, late autumn, early winter,
the northwest, cold, ice, the color red, horses, fruit on trees, etc.

In terms of medical *I Ching* divination, *Qian*, the Creative, is associated with
diseases of the head, brain, spinal cord, and the central nervous system. It also
suggests or corresponds to severe diseases or symptoms and malignancies. As
far as psychological states are concerned, this trigram indicates extreme mental
and emotional states. Its phase correspondence is metal.

2. *Dui (Tui)*, the Joyous, Lake, Marsh

————— ————— This trigram has two yang or solid lines at the bottom and one
——————————— yin or broken line at the top. Thus it symbolizes joy, a lake, or
——————————— a marsh. To the ancient Chinese, a marsh exemplified a place
of joyous life with water, plants, fish, birds, and other animals. It also connotes
pleasure, bliss, cheer, enjoyment, fun, gaiety, gladness, happiness, delight,
ecstasy, exhilaration, harmony, accord, agreement, unanimity, reconciliation,
calm, serenity, tranquility, peace, indulgence, extravagance, luxury, stars, the
third daughter, mid-autumn, the west, sheep, young girls, etc.

Dui, the Joyous, corresponds in the realm of health and medicine to diseases
of the mouth, oral cavity, the digestive system, and reproductive system. It also
suggests chronic diseases, a slow onset, and long-term sequelae as well as diet,
nutrition, and sexual factors playing a factor in the patient's case. This trigram
relates to the metal phase in five phase theory. In terms of psychology, it
indicates overexcitement and frenzied states of mind.

3. *Li (Li)*, the Clinging, Fire

This trigram has one yin line between two yang lines and it signifies the clinging or fire. Since it resembles a Chinese character for the eye, it came to symbolize light, brightness, luminescence, glowing, radiance, incandescence, gleaming, brilliance, the sun, heat, vision, magnificence, resplendence, decoration, the second daughter, mid-summer, the south, soldiers, animals with a hard shell, etc.

Li, the Clinging, corresponds to circulatory diseases and cardiovascular conditions as well as diseases of the small intestine, tongue, and eyes. It suggests inflammation, fever, and erythema or redness and also problems with the metabolism. In general, this trigram relates to the fire phase and all that that phase connotes in the realm of Chinese medicine. Occasionally, extreme forms of delirium and hysteria can be indicated by this trigram.

4. *Zhen (Chen)*, the Arousing, Thunder

This *gua* or trigram has only one yang line at the bottom and two yin or broken lines on top. It represents the arousing or thunder. It also implies rapidness, fastness, quick movement, lightening, excitation, shaking, agitation, irritation, stimulation, dashing, bolting, liveliness, dynamic energy, suddenness, acuteness, abruptness, sharpness, the first son, dragons, mid-spring, the east, the colors black and yellow, streets, boulevards, bamboos shoots, the neighing (of a horse), the green grass of spring, young plants and trees, etc.

Zhen, the Arousing, corresponds to sudden diseases, movable diseases, pain in the nerves, illnesses of the sensory system, motor system, the sympathetic nervous system, the lower extremities, the tendons, gallbladder, and liver yang. It is associated with birth, growth, and development and tends to describe diseases which are painful and which progress quickly, including the possibility of quick recovery. Psychologically, sudden fits of anger and rage may be hinted at by this trigram. Its phase correspondence is wood.

5. *Sun (Sun)*, **the Gentle, Wind, Wood**

This trigram has one yin line at the bottom and two yang lines on top. It is a symbol of the gentle or wind. It also connotes continuous influence, penetration, progress, obedience, slow and quiet movement, pliability, adaptability, changability, flexibility, harmony, the first daughter, late spring, early summer, the southeast, chickens, trees, the color white, smells, aromas, stench, etc.

Sun, the Gentle, corresponds to the wood phase within five phase theory and wind diseases of a gentle and penetrating nature. It also suggests liver yin vacuity, liver wind, the thighs, the parasympathetic nervous system, respiratory and intestinal diseases, gentle or mild illnesses, prolonged recovery, or latent fevers. Psychologically, it is associated with despondency, grief, sorrow, and sadness.

6. *Kan (K'an)*, **the Abysmal, Water**

This *gua* or trigram is just the opposite of *Li*. It is composed of a yang or solid line between two yin or broken lines. It symbolizes the abysmal or water. It also suggests difficulty, impasse, dilemma, danger, risk, jeopardy, disaster, predicament, crisis, peril, obstacle, complication, trouble, affliction, loss of control, adversity, calamities (especially with water), concealment, darkness, poverty, pits, holes, depression, patience, correction, solitude, the second son, mid-winter, the north, pigs, the moon, thieves, etc.

Kan, the Abysmal corresponds to the water phase and diseases of the kidneys, bladder, urogenital system, bones, blood, and body fluids, such as edema. It also suggests the lower abdomen, the marrow, the nose, ears, gums, hair, and eyesight, toxins such as bacteria and viruses and poisons which have accumulated within the body and are stagnant within the system, and cold conditions. Psychologically, it indicates anxiety, worry, fright, fear, phobias, terror, and tension.

7. *Gen (Ken)*, **Keeping Still, Mountain**

The shape of this trigram depicts the outline of a mountain surmounted by the sky with a yang line at the top supported by two yin lines underneath. It is the symbol of keeping still or mountain. It also suggests immobility, stillness, motionlessness, stability, halting, obstacles, a standstill, height, eminence, stubbornness, retreat, cautiousness, eagerness, waiting, saving, refusal, the third son, late winter, early spring, the northeast, dogs, mountain paths, small stones, mice, etc.

Gen, Keeping Still, corresponds to diseases of the head and skull, upper back, neck, and shoulders in particular and the joints in general. It also suggests the male genitalia, diseases which are stuck and do not move, stubborn and immovable obstructions, stoppages in circulation, tumors and constant swellings, loss of resistance, and injuries. In terms of mental/emotional states, it is associated with stubborn, obstinate, and imperturbable states of mind. Its phase correspondence is earth.

8. *Kun (K'un)*, **the Receptive, Earth**

This trigram consists of three broken lines rendering this the most yin trigram of the eight. Traditionally, it is represented by the docility and strength of a mare or mother cow. It synbolizes the receptive or earth. It also indicates receptivity, passivity, submissiveness, a yielding quality, hidden activities, secrets, nourishment, quiet, industriousness, evenness, patience, endurance, peacefulness, voidness, virtuousness, humility, kindness, resourcefulness, femininity, delicacy, devotion, woven cloth, cooking pots, acquisitiveness, frugality, wagons, carriages, the art of writing, mother, late summer, early winter, the southwest, the color black, etc.

Kun, the Receptive, corresponds to the earth phase and, therefore, to diseases of the digestive system, the spleen/pancreas and stomach, the female reproductive system, the feet and legs, and subcutaneous tissue. It also occasionally suggests water diseases and typically is associated with chronic, slow moving illnesses. Psychologically, this hexagram suggests depression, despair, and melancholy.

Hexagrams

Although some conjecture that the eight trigrams above were used for a long time for divination purposes, eventually this system was expanded in order to identify more patterns of change and thus more adequately encompass the diversity of experience and phenomena. By adding together two trigrams and, therefore, squaring the total number of possible combinations, 64 six line *gua* or hexagrams were created. With this squaring of the eight trigrams, 64 individual patterns or situations could be described symbolically. Later on, the Duke of Zhou in the 12th Century BC added the concept of the moving line. This idea is based on the fact that when yin reaches its maximum, it transforms into yang and *vice versa*. Since any of the six lines of a hexagram can change or move, this gives a total of 384 individualized patterns or symbols. However, since any or *all* lines in a hexagram may change or move, the actual number of possible permutations is even much greater. By adding the element of moving lines, it was found that, for practical purposes, 64 hexagrams with moving lines are sufficient to describe any phenomena or situation for all human intents and purposes.

When discussing the inner structure of a hexagram, one begins counting the lines from the bottom up. Thus the bottom line is the first line, the next line is the second, and the top line is the sixth. The diagram below shows how each line in a hexagram is numbered according to this scheme. The hexagram pictured is #3, *Zhun (Chun)*, Difficulty at the Beginning.

6th line   ——— ———
5th line   —————————
4th line   ——— ———
3rd line   ——— ———
2nd line   ——— ———
1st line   —————————

Because six line hexagrams are created by adding two three line trigrams together, one above the other, one can also identify and speak of the lower and upper trigrams within a hexagram. The lower trigram composed of lines 1-3 is also sometimes referred to as the inner trigram, and the upper trigram composed of lines 4-6 is sometimes called the outer trigram. In the case of Hexagram 3, *Zhun (Chun)*, Difficulty at the Beginning pictured above, the lower or inner trigram is *Zhen (Chen)*, the Arousing, whereas the upper or outer trigram is *Kan (K'an)*, the Abysmal. As the diagram below shows, when one places *Kan* over *Zhen*, one gets Hexagram 3, *Zhun*.

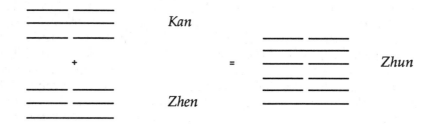

In terms of medical divination, the initial hexagram in most cases represents the patient's current situation. As we will see when we come to describe the medical indications of the hexagrams, a hexagram can both describe a general condition and also suggest specific diseases and patterns.

Moving Lines

When one casts an *I Ching* hexagram by any of the methods described further on in this book, one, several, or even all the lines may turn out to be so-called moving or changing lines. These are lines which are so yin or yang that they are on the verge of changing into their opposite. Thus a yin moving line becomes a yang line and a yang moving line becomes a yin line. In particular, the moving lines in the initial hexagram describe those aspects of the patient which are currently most in flux and are, therefore, those specific places or indications which describe the unique and also pivotal condition of the patient. As we will see below, each hexagram also describes the structure of the body, and moving lines also describe those areas or parts of the body which are diseased.

Nuclear Hexagrams

Within each hexagram there is also another hexagram which is called in English the hidden or nuclear hexagram since it exists at the core of the parent hexagram. If one takes lines 2-4 of a hexagram, these lines constitute the inner or lower nuclear trigram of the nuclear hexagram. Then, lines 3-5 form the outer or upper nuclear trigram of this hidden hexagram. In Hexagram 3, *Zhun*, lines 2-4 form the trigram *Kun* and lines 3-5 form the trigram *Gen*. When *Gen* is placed over *Kun*, this forms Hexagram 23, *Po (Po)*, Splitting Apart. Hexagram 23, *Po* is the hidden or nuclear hexagram within Hexagram 3, *Zhun*.

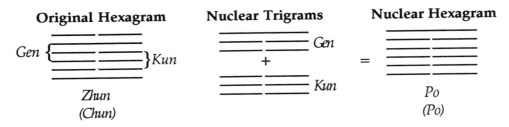

Original Hexagram	Nuclear Trigrams	Nuclear Hexagram

The hidden or nuclear hexagram in almost all cases is a completely new hexagram with its own set of symbolic correspondences and resonances. In medical divination, nuclear trigrams and hidden hexagrams are very important. They typically indicate the roots of a problem hidden underneath the superficial symptomatology. They can guide the physician to the causative etiologies of a disease so that they can correct the source of the problem as opposed to just treating symptoms.

Another interesting fact relating to nuclear trigrams and hidden hexagrams is that, if one continues to create new hidden hexagrams from the nuclear trigrams within each preceding hexagram, they all will eventually become either *Kun (K'un)* or *Qian (Ch'ien)*. In other words, they all boil down eventually to yin or yang. This suggests that the ultimate root of all disease is imbalance of yin and yang which, in the human body, manifest primarily as qi and blood.

Progressed Hexagrams

When one changes the moving lines to their opposites, one gets the so-called progressed or new hexagram. Each moving line represents yin or yang at its apogee and so is in the process or on the verge of changing into its opposite. A yin moving line thus becomes yang and a yang moving line thus becomes yin. When one makes these changes within the initial hexagram, one gets a new hexagram which is called the progressed hexagram. For example, if in Hexagram 7, *Shi (Shih)*, the Army, lines 2 and 6 are moving, this results in the progressed Hexagram 23, *Po (Po)*, Splitting Apart. The diagram below shows this progression.

Original Hexagram	New Hexagram
7	23
Shi	*Po*
(*Shih*)	(*Po*)

In medical *I Ching* divination, the progressed hexagram symbolizes the likely course the patient's condition may take in the near future. Thus the progressed hexagram describes the patient's prognosis. This can be very helpful to the physician in determining the severity and probable course of the patient's disease.

Interrelationships Between the Lines

Correct & Incorrect Positions

There are right positions and wrong positions for the lines in the *I Ching* in the sense of appropriate or healthy, propitious norms. Traditionally, the 1st or beginning line, the 3rd, and the 5th lines are correct when occupied by a yang or solid line and incorrect when occupied by a yin or broken line. On the contrary, the 2nd, 4th, and 6th lines are correct when occupied by a yin line and incorrect when occupied by a yang line. Below is an example of a hexagram with perfect positioning of yin and yang, broken and solid lines.

63 *Ji Ji (Chi Chi)*, After Completion

6th line, correct position for yin	___ ___
5th line, correct position for yang	_____
4th line, correct position for yin	___ ___
3rd line, correct position for yang	_____
2nd line, correct position for yin	___ ___
1st line, correct position for yang	_____

Because all the lines in the above hexagram are correctly positioned, this hexagram conveys a sense of completion. Thus it is named After Completion.

Another example is Hexagram 40, *Xie (Hsieh)*, Deliverance.

6th line, correct position for yin	___ ___
5th line, incorrect position for yin	___ ___
4th line, incorrect position for yang	_____
3rd line, incorrect position for yin	___ ___
2nd line, incorrect position for yang	_____
1st line, incorrect position for yin	___ ___

In this hexagram, there is only one position occupied by a correct yin line. All the other positions are occupied by incorrect lines. This suggests the idea of deliverance which is the name of this hexagram.

In medical divination, a line in a correct position denotes strength, while a line in an incorrect position suggests weakness. In the case of Hexagram 40 or Deliverance, a great amount of weakness is suggested by five lines in incorrect positions. This connotes an extremely delicate condition or the death of the patient.

Correspondence & Juxtaposition

In terms of relationships between individual lines, there are two kinds identified by students and users of the *I Ching*. These are called *ying* or correspondence and *bi*, juxtaposition.

A *ying* or resonance relationship is a correspondence in terms of yin and yang between the 1st or lowest line and the 4th, the 2nd and the 5th, and the 3rd and 6th or top lines. If these lines are occupied by a yin and a yang line respectively, the relationship is called *zheng ying* or correct correspondence. If these lines are occupied by a yin and yin line or a yang and a yang line, this is called *bu ying* or no or incorrect correspondence.

Hexagram 4, *Meng (Mêng)*, Youthful Folly, is an example of a *ying* relationship.

6th line	—————————
5th line	———— ————
4th line	———— ————
3rd line	———— ————
2nd line	—————————
1st line	———— ————

In this particular hexagram, the 1st or beginning line is broken or yin and the 4th line, its corresponding or resonating line, is also yin. Therefore, the relationship between these two lines is said to be *bu ying* or not resonant, not corresponding. On the other hand, the 2nd line is solid or yang and the 5th line is broken or yin. This forms a *zheng ying* or correct correspondence or resonance. Further, the 3rd line is yin and the sixth or top line is yang. This thus forms another *zheng ying* relationship.

Bi or juxtaposition, ratio, or proportion describes the yin yang relationship between any two lines which are positioned next to each other, for instance, the 1st and 2nd or 5th and 6th lines. Hexagram 28, *Da Guo (Ta Kuo),* Preponderance of the Great, is an example of *bi* relationship.

6th line	——— ———
5th line	—————
4th line	—————
3rd line	—————
2nd line	—————
1st line	——— ———

In this hexagram, the 1st line is yin and the 2nd line is yang. Therefore, these two lines are in good yin yang relationship to each other. They complement and counterbalance each other. This is called *zheng bi* or correct juxtaposition or proportion. However, the relationship between the 2nd and 3rd, 3rd and 4th, and 4th and 5th lines are all in a yang to yang configuration. This renders them not proportional or correctly juxtaposed. In Chinese, this is called *bu bi*. Of the remaining lines, only the top two, lines 5 and 6, are in a *zheng bi* relationship. It is the preponderance of lines which are incorrectly juxtaposed or *bu bi* which gives rise to this hexagrams name, Preponderance of the Great, *i.e.,* preponderance of yang.

In medical *I Ching* divination, correct *zheng ying* and *zheng bi* relationships signify abundance of *zheng* or righteous qi and healthy balance within the organism. Whereas, *bu ying* and *bu bi* relationships indicate weakness, vacuity, or imbalance at the places where they occur. It is very important to pay attention to these line relationships when interpreting a hexagram.

Hexagrams as Anatomical Representations

There are three main ways *I Ching* hexagrams represent body parts. First, the *I Ching* sometimes utilizes the names of hexagrams and moving line readings to suggest body parts. Hexagram 27, *Yi (I)*, Corners of the Mouth, is a good example of a hexagram's name indicating a body part, in this case the mouth. (It also by extension suggests nutrition.) The moving line readings of Hexagram 31, *Xian (Hsien)*, Influence (Wooing), are good examples of line judgements suggesting body parts or anatomical locations. For example, the judgement for the 1st line states, "One sense their big toes." The 2nd line's judgement reads, "One senses their calves." And the 3rd line reads, "One senses their thighs", etc.

Secondly, each of the eight *gua* or trigrams symbolize or are associated with different body parts. The *I Ching* commentary, the *Shuo Gua (Discussion of Trigrams)* states:

> *Qian* symbolizes the head. *Kun* symbolizes the abdomen. *Zhen* symbolizes the feet. *Sun* symbolizes the thighs. *Kan* symbolizes the ears. *Li* symbolizes the eyes. *Gen* symbolizes the hands. *Dui* symbolizes the mouth.[6]

Third, the six lines of a hexagram can be seen as a symbolic representation of the human body and this can be very important when doing medical divination. When seen from this point of view, the 1st line represents the feet. The 2nd line represents the legs and lower back. The 3rd line connotes the lower burner. In Chinese medicine, the *xia jiao* or lower burner is the anatomical part of the torso from the navel or waist to the base of the perineum. Line 4 represents the *zhong jiao* or middle burner. This is the anatomical part of the torso from the waist to the hypochondrium or just below the ribs. Line 5 represents the chest or *shang jiao*, upper burner. And line 6 symbolizes the area above the neck. The diagram below describes these symbolic anatomical relationships.

---

[6]   Shang Bing-he, *Zhou Yi Shang Shi Xue (Master Shang's Study of the Zhou Yi)*, China Publishing House, Beijing, 1979, p. 326

6th line = anything above the neck
5th line = chest, upper burner
4th line = epigastrium, middle burner
3rd line = hypogastrium, lower burner
2nd line = legs, lower back
1st line = feet

The Representation of Time in *I Ching* Symbology

The concept of time is represented in the *I Ching* in several ways. First, it may be suggested by the name of the hexagram. For example, Hexagram 3, *Zhun (Chun)*, Difficulty at the Beginning, suggests, *vis à vis* medical divination, the onset or early stage of an illness. On the other hand, Hexagram 23, *Po (Po)*, Splitting Apart, implies the terminal stage of a disease where yin and yang are splitting apart. Thus one can usually relate the concept of time to the name of the hexagram. At the same time, the content of the symbolism of the whole hexagram, not just the name itself, may also connote time. For instance, Hexagram 11, *Tai (T'ai)*, Peace, signifies a very stable condition where time, *i.e.*, change, is proceeding in a slow manner. Whereas, Hexagram 7, *Shi (Shih)*, The Army, symbolizes the fast and dynamic movement of time or change.

Another way the *I Ching* represents time is by the lines themselves. Traditionally, the 1st line denotes the starting point of an event or process, while the 6th line implies the end of that event or process. For example, if one has a cancer patient and one wants to know where they stand in terms of the time of their illness, one can cast the *I Ching*. Say one obtains a hexagram with a moving line in the 2nd position and, through taking the patient's history, one also knows that the patient was diagnosed with the cancer 6 months ago, in this case the moving line in the 2nd position suggests the patient's illness is still in its early stage of development. However, if one obtains a changing line in the 6th position, even though the patient has been diagnosed with cancer for only 6 months, the *I Ching* is suggesting that they are terminal. Thus the position of a changing line is extremely important in terms of conceptualizing time in medical divination.

24

Nevertheless, there is no fixed length of time allotted for a line, trigram, or hexagram. A line or trigram may suggest a day in case of an acute illness or a year in a chronic disease. Thus the amount of time suggested by any element of a hexagram needs to be decided based on the condition and situation of each particular case. Otherwise, one's interpretations would become mechanical and simplistic, not to mention wrong.

Gui Hun Hexagrams

Gui means to return or gather. *Hun* refers to the ethereal soul as opposed to the *po* or corporeal soul. *Gui hun* hexagrams are those in which the upper and lower trigrams become the same when the yin yang polarity of the 5th line is switched. Hexagram 13, *Tong Ren (T'ung Jen)*, Fellowship of Men, is an example of a *gui hun* hexagram.

As one can see, if the 5th line of this hexagram is changed from yang to yin, it becomes Hexagram 30, *Li (Li)*, the Clinging. This is composed of two *Li* trigrams, one above the other. The eight *gui hun* hexagrams are 7, *Shi (Shih)*, the Army; 8, *Bi (Pi)*, Holding Together; 13, *Tong Ren (T'ung Jen)*, Fellowship of Men; 14, *Da You (Ta Yu)*, Possession in Great Measure; 17, *Sui (Sui)*, Following; 18, *Gu (Ku)*, Work on What Has Been Spoiled; 53, *Jian (Chien)*, Development; and 54, *Gui Mei (Kuei Mei)*, Marrying Maiden.

The *gui hun* hexagrams are considered inauspicious because they symbolically suggest the soul or *hun* returning to its origin, *i.e.*, death.

You Hun Hexagrams

Another group of hexagrams is called *you hun* or wandering soul hexagrams.

These are also deemed unfavorable because they connote such conditions as coma or near-death when the soul wanders around outside the body. *You hun* hexagrams are those which, when their 5th line's polarity is switched, the upper and lower trigrams become polar opposites. Hexagram 35, *Jin (Chin)*, Progress, is an example of a *you hun* hexagram.

If one changes its 5th line from yin to yang, one gets hexagram 12, *Pi (Pi)*, Standstill (Stagnation). In this hexagram, the upper trigram, *Qian*, is the polar opposite of the lower trigram, *Kun*.

The eight *you hun* hexagrams are 5, *Xu (Hsu)*, Waiting; 6, *Song (Sung)*, Conflict; 27, *Yi (I)*, Corners of the Mouth; 28, *Da Guo (Ta Kuo)*, Preponderance of the Great; 35, *Jin (Chin)*, Progress; 36, *Ming Yi (Ming I)*, Darkening of the Light; 61, *Zhong Fu (Chung Fu)*, Inner Truth; and 62, *Xiao Guo (Xiao Kuo)*, Preponderance of the Small.

In medical divination, both *gui hun* and *you gui* hexagrams are considered inauspicious and sinister portents indicating possible higher morbidity and mortality than other hexagrams. Traditionally, *gui hun* hexagrams have been strongly associated with death and dying by many *I Ching* masters. While *you hun* hexagrams have been associated with near-death or comatose conditions.

3

Casting the *I Ching*

Preliminary Requirements

A Quiet Place & A Quiet Mind

Before one begins asking questions of this ancient oracle, one should first find a quiet place where they will not be distracted. This place should be serene and comfortable, a place where one can enter into a meditative state of mind. In order to get good results from *I Ching* divination, it is extremely important that casting the oracle be carried out in a peaceful, nonjudgmental frame of mind. If one tries to cast the *I Ching* in a hurried, perturbed state of mind, one will never be able to obtain a proper answer to their question.

In order to enter a calm state of mind, it is most helpful to practice some form of meditation on a daily basis. It does not matter what exact method of meditation one uses as long as one finds it personally compatible and one is able, thereby, to enter a deeply relaxed, tranquil state of mind. If chanting is conducive to entering a meditative state, one may incorporate it during their daily practice. If one has never meditated before, I strongly urge the reader to find a meditation instructor whom one can really trust and from whom one can learn how to meditate. I do not recommend beginners meditate without a teacher. Unguided practice of meditation is risky and dangerous. While one meditates, various hidden feelings and emotions may surface and one may not know how to handle these. It is, therefore, imperative for beginners to have supervision while learning meditation of any kind.

Formulating the Question

When one has achieved an appropriate level of calmness within oneself, one can begin formulating their question. During this process, I strongly advise the reader to write down all their questions. In my personal experience, by writing one's questions down on a piece of paper and by looking at them, one's subconscious mind can concentrate on these questions better than by just repeating them over and over again in their head. This process of writing also serves the purpose of recording one's *I Ching* consultation. I recommend getting a notebook specially designated for this purpose. One can then also register their answers, impressions, and interpretations in this. After working with the *I Ching* for some time, one's notebook will become a precious gift to oneself.

When asking the *I Ching* questions, it is also very important to make sure that one formulates simple questions rather than long, convoluted ones. In my experience, the simpler the question, the better the results of *I Ching* divination. For example, two separate questions such as, "Should I change this patient's formula?" and "What is the prognosis of this patient's flu?" are better questions than, "Should I change his herbal prescription next Monday, if he had recovered from his flu?". It is also not advisable to ask an either/or type question like, "Will she get better or worse?" Instead, one should simply ask a question like, "Will she get better?" and see what the *I Ching* has to say about the particular patient. Above all, if one already knows the answer to their question or if one can determine what to do by thinking consciously and systematically, one should not exasperate one's higher intelligence by asking insignificant questions that can be solved in a normal way.

In terms of formulating an individual question, it is most important to know what one wants to ask the *I Ching*. When people get an obscure answer, it is usually because that they were not clear about what they wanted to know. When one asks a question of the *I Ching*, one is ultimately asking their deep instinctive mind to come up with an answer and, if one is not clear about what one wants to know, they will only get a nebulous answer. Therefore, it is extremely important to contemplate one's question and ask oneself whether or not one knows what they want.

Another important thing about asking a question of the *I Ching* is that one should ask a particular question only once. Never ask the same question twice just because one does not like the answer one has obtained. I know some people who keep asking the same question over and over again in a different form until they get the answer that they want to hear. *This should never be done.* When one is dealing with the *I Ching*, they are dealing with the sacred part of one's higher intelligence and to keep asking the same question is nothing but an insult to one's essential being. As an extension of this, one should also not cast the *I Ching* frivolously on insignificant matters because that also is a humiliation of the dignity of one's inmost mind. Further, if one uses the *I Ching* in an unethical way, one should know that, in one way or another, one will pay for it. For example, I used to know an man who, for a long time, used the *I Ching* for gambling and made quite a bit of money. However, he eventually lost everything he had, including his own life! This was a good example of what may happen when one continuously abuses their subconscious intelligence.

Tools Necessary for Casting the *I Ching*

There are many ways to cast the *I Ching*. Although, traditionally, *I Ching* sticks made from yarrow stalks or bamboo were considered the proper tools for casting the oracle, past practitioners of the *I Ching* have invented many tools and techniques for consulting it.

First, there is the three coin technique of divination which has already become quite popular in the West. There is also a casting method utilizing dice which is very quick and really convenient in daily practice. And, finally, in our high technology days, there are several computer software programs for *I Ching* divination! They are fairly quick and well designed and are very good learning tools.

Personally, I must state that I like the traditional *I Ching* stalks or sticks best, partly because I like the meditative sounds and feeling of the sticks when I shuffle them, and partly because I like the feeling of connection between myself and the sticks as compared to coins or dice I must throw out of my hands. However, to become good at using the stick technique requires a great amount of dexterity and years of practice. It is like learning how to play the violin. I have seen several great *I Ching* masters manipulate their sticks in such a magnificent way that the whole casting process appeared to be a splendid ritual. Those people had worked with their *I Ching* sticks every day for so many years that the sticks naturally looked like a part of their hands. If one is an *I Ching* beginner yet wants to start using the sticks, one should take their time and practice slowly. This method is the best system and one should eventually learn it. It is worth practicing.

As far as the material for the sticks is concerned, one can make a good set of bamboo sticks from 10-inch long, thick barbecue sticks that can be bought at most regular supermarkets. One needs 50 sticks. All one needs do is to cut their sharp ends off and to sand them well so as not to get stuck with splinters. If one wants to make them very smooth to the touch, they may want to wax them by rubbing them lightly on a candle. If one wants to stain the sticks, use a dark wood stain before waxing.[1]

If one is not ready to work with the traditional stick method, one may choose to use the three coin technique. In that case, all one needs are three coins one likes to use for this purpose. They can be large or small coins as long as one is comfortable with them. However, they should all be of the same kind and the same size. One should not use two large and one small coin. They should also have clearly designated head and tail sides to them. If they have similar designs on both sides, they may be too confusing to use.

---

[1]   Those interested in purchasing professional tools for *I CHing* divination may call or write J.A.A.F., Inc. at (415) 924-2910, 21 Tamal Vista Blvd., Suite 110, Corte Madera, CA 94925. Most professional *I Ching* practitioners have a set of *I Ching* sticks (*zei chi ku*), stand for these sticks (*zei tou*), and a set of six scoring sticks (*san gi*).

If one wants to use the dice method, all one needs is two octagonal dice (with eight sides) of two different colors and one regular hexagonal dice (with six sides) of any color. These are usually available at drug or game and novelty stores. The octagonal dice should have eight numbers from 1-8 and the hexagonal dice should have six numbers from 1-6.

Finally, if one is interested in consulting the *I Ching* by computer, there are various programs available on the market for different types of system configuration.[2]

Although each of these various casting methods involve different processes, one can obtain the answers they needs from the *I Ching* by any of these techniques. I believe that the most important aspect of any divinatory processes is not the method of divination but the skills of the diviner. In other words, one may obtain as much information from the stick method as from the dice technique. It all depends on one's skills as an operator and interpreter of the *I Ching* oracle. I do not personally believe that any particular system of divination is superior to any other methods. Therefore, one need not confine oneself to any one system all the time. What is important here is to find a system that serves each individual and each circumstance best.

Obtaining a Hexagram

The process of *I Ching* divination consists of two phases. The first phase is called casting. This refers to the meditative and mathematical procedure of obtaining a hexagram. The second phase is called interpretation. Interpretation is discussed in detail in the next chapter.

---

[2]   I have used a program called *I-Ching* from The Software Toolworks, 19808 Nordhoff Place, Chatsworth, CA 91311, (818) 885-9000. This is a very good example of such computerized *I Ching* educational tools. Another good program is *I Ching* by Kerson Huang, P.O.Box 1083, Marblehead, MA 01945, (617) 631-5985.

The purpose of the casting procedure is to come up with a hexagram and there are various ways of manifesting a hexagram. As mentioned above, one can come up with a hexagram by casting coins, dice, *I Ching* sticks, or even by pushing computer buttons. Each method has its own benefits over others. For example, the quickest method is the dice technique. It can give one a hexagram in literally a second. This is a great system to use when one needs to cast the *I Ching* many times a day. Computer systems are usually the second fastest method of obtaining a *gua* or hexagram. They are also very easy to use. However, they do require relatively expensive hardware and as well as software that can run from $5-75. The coin toss method requires six throws and it is a bit more time consuming than the dice technique. However, it can generate more symbolical ramifications for each line of the hexagram than the dice technique. The traditional stick methods are the most time consuming and they require a lot of mental concentration. However, these techniques have the merit of giving one even greater delineation than any other method. It is also the most meditative of all. Since the traditional stick methods take a lot of time and energy to carry through, especially the most complicated traditional method which requires 18 divisions of the sticks, these may be reserved only for very special and auspicious occasions. What I personally recommend is to become familiar with various techniques so that one can choose the most appropriate method for different purposes whenever one wants to cast the *I Ching*.

The Dice Method

The dice technique is the easiest and quickest of all techniques discussed in this book. It is an excellent system for beginners to learn to get into the habit of casting the *I Ching* every day.

In this particular method of casting, as mentioned in the previous section, one needs two octagonal dice of two different colors with the numbers 1-8 and one hexagonal (regular) dice of any color with the numbers 1-6. A dice cup is optional. One uses one of the two octagonal dice for determining the upper trigram and the other die for the lower trigram. The hexagonal die is used for determining the changing line. For example, I have one red octagonal die, one green octagonal die, and one white hexagonal die in my dice cup. I have designated the red die for the upper trigram, the green die for the lower trigram, and the white die for the changing line. Traditionally, one trigram corresponds to each number on the octagonal die in the following order:

1	2	3	4
Qian (Ch'ien)	Dui (Tui)	Li (Li)	Zhen (Chen)
the Creative Heaven	the Joyous Lake	the Clinging Fire	the Arousing Thunder

5	6	7	8
Sun (Sun)	Kan (K'an)	Gen (Ken)	Kun (K'un)
the Gentle Wind	the Abysmal Water	the Keeping Still Mountain	the Receptive Earth

For example, I ask a question and roll the three dice. I obtain 4 on the red die (upper trigram), 1 on the green die (lower trigram), and 5 on the white die (changing line). This means that the upper trigram is 4 *Zhen* (*Chen*), the lower trigram is 1, *Qian* (*Ch'ien*), and the changing line is 5. This constitutes Hexagram 34, *Da Zhuang* (*Ta Chuang*), the Power of the Great, with the fifth line changing from yin to yang. Thus the new or progressed hexagram is Hexagram 43, *Guai* (*Kuai*), Breakthrough. This process is illustrated below.

33

Original Hexagram	New Hexagram
34	43

4 on red dice ——x—— (5 on white dice)

→

1 on green dice

Da Zhuang
(Ta Chuang)

Guai
(Kuai)

Thus, the dice casting technique is simple and quick. However, in this method, one may only obtain a single changing line. Whereas, in the coin toss technique, one can get changing up to six changing lines. On the one hand, the dice method is very good, because it is easy and does not require a great deal of mental concentration. On the other hand, it is often deficient in delineating the specifics of a situation. This is, therefore, a good method when one wants to ask a fast and easy question like, "Should I treat this patient next week?", or, "Should I add Rhubarb to this formula?".

The Coin Toss Method

The coin toss method involves throwing onto a flat surface three coins simultaneously six times in succession to obtain a single hexagram. In other words, one throws the three coins once for each line, from bottom line to top. Whereas one only has to throw the three dice once in the dice method.

First of all, one must decide which side of the coins one is using is the head and which side the tail. One should be clear about their distinction and must not change their designation once it has been made. For example, if one is using three pennies with a picture of Abraham Lincoln on one side, that side should be called the head, while the side with the Lincoln Memorial Building should be called the tail. Traditionally, a head indicates yang and has the numerical value of 3, whereas a tail denotes yin and its numerical value is 2. Thus, by throwing three pennies at one time, there are four possible yin/yang combinations as follows:

1) *Tai yin* (Supreme or Changing yin)
Tail (2) + Tail (2) + Tail (2) = 6   (———x———)

2) *Shao yang* (Lesser or Fixed yang)
Tail (2) + Tail (2) + Head (3) = 7   (—————)

3) *Shao yin* (Lesser or Fixed yin)
Tail (2) + Head (3) + Head (3) = 8 (——— ———)

4) *Tai yang* (Supreme or Changing yang)
Head (3) + Head (3) + Head (3) = 9 (———o———)

As seen above, three tails gives 6 and is called changing or moving yin because it is too yin to be stable. Thus yin in the extreme changes into yang. Two tails and one head add up numerically to 7 which is yang and fixed. One tail and two heads add up to 8 which is a nice yin and is fixed. Finally, three heads add up to 9 which is too yang to stay balanced and must change into yin for better balance. Thus, every time one casts the coins, they need to add up the numbers and find out whether the resulting number corresponds to a yin line or a yang line and whether it is fixed or changing.

For example, one asks a question and throws the three coins six times. The first casting comes up two heads and one tail which add up to 8 or fixed yin. The second casting comes up three heads which add up to 9 for a changing yang line to yin. The third casting comes up three tails which add up to 6 and a changing yin line to a yang. The fourth and fifth castings both happen to come up two tails and a head which add up to 7, fixed yang lines. And finally, the last casting comes up three heads or 9 for a changing yang line. The following diagram shows the results of this process.

35

Original Hexagram		New Hexagram
6		**31**

9 (Changing yang)	——o——	6th line ➡	——— ———
7 (Fixed yang)	—————	5th line	—————
7 (Fixed yang)	—————	4th line	—————
6 (Changing yin)	——x——	3rd line ➡	—————
9 (Changing yang)	——o——	2nd line ➡	——— ———
8 (Fixed yin)	——— ———	1st line	——— ———

Song
(*Sung*)

Xian
(*Hsien*)

Thus the coin method is a little more involved and complex than the dice method but, as one can see from the above example, one can obtain far more symbolical differentiations than the dice method since one can obtain any or all six moving lines. In medical divination, this is a good technique for asking questions which deal with complex and intricate situations such as diagnosis.

The Stick or Stalk Method

Traditionally, there are three levels of complexity in stick divination methodology: full divination, intermediate divination, and simplified divination.

Many scholars believe that the full divination method is the original divination method used at the time of the Zhou Dynasty in ancient China when the *I Ching* was compiled.[9] It requires three castings per line and, therefore, 18 castings of sticks to come up with one hexagram. This requires a great deal of time and concentration, and it is usually reserved for divination on extremely critical and essential matters, such as an issue of life and death.

---

[9]   For example, *Kato Daigaku Daikoza (Comprehensive Lectures on the Study of the Yi Jing)*, Kigen Shobo, 8 Vols., Tokyo, Vol. 1, p.144 (in Japanese)

The intermediate divination method is a greatly simplified technique compared to the full divination method. It only requires one casting of sticks per line, six castings in all to obtain a hexagram. In this respect, it is the same as the coin toss technique. This is the most frequently used method by professional *I Ching* readers on various subjects of medium importance, such as the moving of residence, the auspiciousness of a marriage, business decisions, etc. In medical divination, this method is very suitable for asking questions on diagnosis and prognosis.

The simplified divination method is an extremely uncomplicated casting method requiring only three divisions of the sticks — the first separation for the lower trigram, the second for the upper trigram, and the last for the changing line. Because one obtains trigrams instead of individual lines, this method is similar to the dice method. This method is a quick and simple way of casting the *I Ching* many times a day on matters of small importance.

Casting the Sticks

All three methods of casting the sticks begin the same. After meditating in a quiet room and writing down one's question, one picks up the 50 sticks in a single bundle and bows to the sticks. This is to show respect and reverence to the whole procedure of casting. Next one takes a single stick out from the bunch and places it to one side. If one has a stand for their *I Ching* sticks, place this stick in that stand. This particular stick which is set to one side is called the *tai ji* or supreme ultimate. It represents the level of spiritual existence or absolute reality beyond the realm of relative existence. This is why it is not manipulated with the rest of the sticks. Next, one holds up the remaining 49 sticks in their hands and shuffles them for while until one's mind becomes calmed by the sound of the rubbing sticks. At this point, one stops shuffling and transfers all the sticks to their left hand. Then spread the sticks evenly with the right hand in the shape of a fan. Hold the sticks up to the height of one's face and about one inch away from it. Seen from without, one looks like a person covering their face with a fan. Take a deep breath and, as one exhales, divide the sticks into two by quickly grabbing a bunch of sticks with the right hand. Now, one has one bunch of sticks in their left hand and another bunch of sticks in their right. Put the bunch in the right hand down on the right side of one's desk while holding the ones in the left hand. The group of sticks on the desk is traditionally called earth, whereas the sticks in one's left hand are called heaven. Take a single stick out with one's right hand and place the lower end of it between the left little finger and the fourth finger. This stick is called humanity. Now, there are four kinds of sticks, the *tai ji* stick, the earth sticks, the human stick, and the heaven sticks. It is very important to have a clear understanding of their differentiation in order to obtain correct results.

This initial dividing of the sticks corresponds to Zhu Xi's division of reality into absolute and relative, and relative reality into the *san cai* or three capabilities. Thus, casting the *I Ching* recreates the unfoldment of the universe or the so-called ten thousand things. As such, this ritual is fraught with great metaphysical significance.

The Full Divination Method

As mentioned above, this technique demands a great amount of time and energy. Since *I Ching* beginners will have a difficult time carrying out this whole process, I do not recommend this method to anyone who has not practiced other of the above methods for at least a year. Especially if one is not used to concentrating intensely for half an hour or more, one will end up making mistakes by losing their concentration during the course of this process. Nonetheless, the process of this traditional divination is a very beautiful and magnificent experience.

One begins this particular method exactly the same as any other stick method. After meditating, one picks up the 50 sticks in a single bundle. Then one takes one stick out from the bunch and places it aside. Again this stick is the *tai ji* stick. Next, hold up the remaining 49 sticks in one's hands and shuffle them for a while until one feels that they have gotten an answer from the *I Ching*. Then stop shuffling and transfer all the sticks to one's left hand. Spread the sticks evenly with the right hand in the shape of a fan and hold them up to the height of one's face. Take a deep breath and, while exhaling, divide the sticks quickly into two with the right hand. Put the bunch in one's right hand down on the right side of one's desk. This becomes the earth bundle. Then, while holding onto the sticks in one's left hand, *i.e.*, the heaven bundle, remove a single stick with one's right hand and place the lower end of this stick between the left little finger and the fourth finger. This stick represents humanity.

From this point on, one begins the various counting procedures which produce a hexagram. In this ancient technique, one needs to go through three counting processes per line or a total of 18 countings for the entire hexagram. This may sound very complicated, but the underlining principles are very simple.

Begin by counting off the sticks in one's left hand (heaven) by fours. Place each successive group of four sticks down on the left side of one's desk. When four or less than four sticks are left, place the remaining stick(s) with the right hand between one's left middle and ring (fourth) fingers. The possible number of remaining sticks at this point is 1, 2, 3, or 4. Then pick up the sticks that one previously placed on the right side of the desk (earth) and count these off by fours. When four or less than four sticks are left, place the remaining sticks between one's left middle and index fingers. The possible number of remaining sticks is again 1, 2, 3, or 4. Now add up all the sticks that one has placed between their left fingers and the total number of those sticks must be either 5 or 9. The possibilities are $1 + 4 + 4 = 9, 1 + 3 + 1 = 5, 1 + 2 + 2 = 5,$ or $1 + 1 + 3 = 5.$

After this first counting off of the sticks, the human stick that one placed between their left little and fourth fingers is discarded as surplus. Therefore, 9 is counted as 8 and 5 as 4. However, traditionally 8 is regarded as an inferior numerical unit, and only the value of 2 is given to it. Whereas the number 4 is considered as a superior numerical unit, and the value 3 is allocated to it. Therefore, if 9 sticks all together are left between one's fingers, these are given the value of 2, while if 5 sticks are left, one counts these as 3. After this first calculation, place those sticks on the right side of the desk for the time being. One has just completed the first of the three calculations for the first (bottom) line of a hexagram.

Now, pick up all the remaining sticks (except the ones put aside on the desk). Shuffle these for a minute while meditating as above. After shuffling, hold the sticks up in front of one's face and spread them evenly like a fan. Take a deep breath and while exhaling, quickly divide the sticks into two. Take the sticks now in one's right hand (earth) and place them down on the desk. Pick one stick from this bunch on the desk and place it between the left little and fourth fingers. This represents or corresponds to humanity. Count off the sticks that are now in one's left hand (heaven) by fours as above and place the remaining stick(s) between the fourth and middle fingers. The possible number is 1, 2, 3, or 4. Then pick up the sticks from the desk (earth) and count these off by fours again. Place the remaining sticks between one's middle and index fingers. The possible number is 1, 2, 3, or 4. Now count all the sticks collected between one's left fingers. This time the sum of the remaining sticks is either 8 or 4. The possible combinations are 1 + 4 + 3 = 8, 1 + 3 + 4 = 8, 1 + 1 + 2 = 4, or 1 + 2 + 1 = 4.) Give the numerical value of 2 for 8 and 3 for 4. This completes the second step of the three steps to form the first line.

For the third time, repeat exactly the same procedure for the second casting and again the sum of the remaining sticks is either 8 or 4. Again 8 accounts for 2 and 4 counts for 3 in value.

Now add all the numerical values from each process to form the first line. The following diagram provides all the possible number combinations and their names.

1) *Tai yin* (Total value = 6) (Changing yin)

Remainder :	9 sticks (= 8, Value = 2)
+	8 sticks (= 8, Value = 2)
+	8 sticks (= 8, Value = 2)
	Total Value = 6

2) *Shao yang* (Total value = 7) (Fixed yang)

a) Remainder :   9 sticks (= 8, Value = 2)

           +   8 sticks (= 8, Value = 2)

           +   4 sticks (= 4, Value = 3)

                    Total Value = 7

b) Remainder :   5 sticks (= 4, Value = 3)

           +   8 sticks (= 8, Value = 2)

           +   8 sticks (= 8, Value = 2)

                    Total Value = 7

c) Remainder :   9 sticks (= 8, Value = 2)

           +   4 sticks (= 4, Value = 3)

           +   8 sticks (= 8, Value = 2)

                    Total Value = 7

3) *Shao yin* (Total value = 8) (Fixed yin)

a) Remainder :   9 sticks (= 8, Value = 2)

           +   4 sticks (= 4, Value = 3)

           +   4 sticks (= 4, Value = 3)

                    Total Value = 8

b) Remainder :   5 sticks (= 4, Value = 3)

           +   5 sticks (= 4, Value = 3)

           +   8 sticks (= 8, Value = 2)

                    Total Value = 8

c) Remainder :   5 sticks (= 4, Value = 3)

           +   8 sticks (= 8, Value = 2)

           +   4 sticks (= 4, Value = 3)

Total Value = 8

4) *Tai yang* (Total value = 9) (Changing yang)

Remainder :   5 sticks (= 4, Value = 3)
+   4 sticks (= 4, Value = 3)
+   4 sticks (= 4, Value = 3)

Total Value = 9

Thus, one needs to repeat these casting procedures six times to form a hexagram or 18 castings in all.

The following is an example of how this full divination works in reality. I have divided the sticks 18 times and obtained:

Line 1 : Remainder   5 sticks (= 4, value = 3)
+   8 sticks (= 8, value = 2)
+   8 sticks (= 8, value = 2)

Total value = 7 (*Shao yang*)

Line 2 : Remainder   9 sticks (= 8, value = 2)
+   8 sticks (= 8, value = 2)
+   8 sticks (= 8, value = 2)

Total value = 6 (*Tai yin*)

Line 3 : Remainder   9 sticks (= 8, value = 2)
+   4 sticks (= 4, value = 3)
+   8 sticks (= 8, value = 2)

Total value = 7 (*Shao yang*)

Line 4 : Remainder   9 sticks (= 8, value = 2)
+   4 sticks (= 4, value = 3)
+   4 sticks (= 4, value = 3)

Total value = 8 (*Shao yin*)

Line 5 : Remainder	9 sticks (= 8, value = 2)
+	4 sticks (= 4, value = 3)
+	8 sticks (= 8, value = 2)

Total value = 7 (*Shao yang*)

Line 6 : Remainder	5 sticks (= 4, value = 3)
+	4 sticks (= 4, value = 3)
+	4 sticks (= 4, value = 3)

Total value = 9 (*Tai yang*)

Therefore, this whole process results in giving the following original hexagram, moving lines, and new hexagram:

Original Hexagram   **New Hexagram**

37   5

6th line	——o——	(from 3 + 3+ 3 = 9) ➟	—— ——
5th line	————	(from 2 + 3 + 2 = 7)	————
4th line	—— ——	(from 2 + 3 + 3 = 8)	—— ——
3rd line	————	(from 2 + 3 + 2 = 7)	————
2nd line	——x——	(from 2 + 2 + 2 = 6) ➟	————
1st line	————	(from 3 + 2 + 2 = 7)	————

Jia Ren   *Xu*
(*Chia Jen*)   (*Hsu*)

As one can see above, the full divination can be a laborious process due to its technical complexity. However, this is the original system of *I Ching* divination and, if one takes the time to practice this technique, it can be a marvelously meditative experience.

The Intermediate Method

Since the full divination takes great amount of time, even professional *I Ching* readers do not routinely use it unless specifically requested. In my own practice of classical Chinese medicine, I typically cast the full divination only once a month. Otherwise, I usually use a simpler method such as the intermediate or simplified techniques described below. What method I chose depends upon my schedule and the matter under consideration.

The intermediate technique is a very excellent system to use for diagnosis and prognosis on a daily basis. In this technique, one only needs to divide the sticks six times instead of 18 times for the full divination. Each division of the sticks determines the nature of the each line, including the changing or fixed quality of the line.

After meditating and removing one stick for *tai ji* out of the 50 sticks, shuffle the sticks and start dividing them exactly the same as in the full divination. First, put down the sticks in one's right hand (earth) on the desk while holding on to the sticks in one's left (heaven). Take one stick out of the pile on the desk (earth) and place it between the left little and fourth fingers. This stands for humanity. Now count off the sticks in the left hand with one's right hand by eights (not by fours as in the full divination) until there are less than 7 sticks remaining in one's left hand. Count the number of the sticks in the left hand and add 1 (human) stick to the sum of these sticks. For example, if there are 7 sticks in one's hand after subtracting by eights, one gets 8 by adding 1. If no stick is left after counting by eights, one gets 1. The number one gets (from 1 to 8) determines the yin/yang quality and the nature (changing or fixed) of the line as follows:

Remainder

a) 1 stick (0 sticks in left hand) + 1 (human stick)
   = *Tai yang* (Changing yang) associated with *Qian* (Heaven)

b) 2 sticks (1 stick in left hand) + 1 (human stick)
 = *Shao yin* (Fixed yin) associated with *Dui* (Marsh)

c) 3 sticks (2 sticks in left hand) + 1 (human stick)
 = *Shao yin* (Fixed yin) associated with *Li* (Fire)

d) 4 sticks (3 sticks in left hand) + 1 (human stick)
 = *Shao yang* (Fixed yang) associated with *Zhen* (Thunder)

e) 5 sticks (4 sticks in left hand) + 1 (human stick)
 = *Shao yin* (Fixed yin) associated with *Sun* (Wind)

f) 6 sticks (5 sticks in left hand) + 1 (human stick)
 = *Shao yang* (Fixed yang) associated *Kan* (Water)

g) 7 sticks (6 sticks in left hand) + 1 (human stick)
 = *Shao yang* (Fixed yang) associated *Gen* (Mountain)

h) 8 sticks (7 sticks in left hand) + 1 (human stick)
 = *Tai yin* (Changing yin) associated with *Kun* (Earth)

As one can see above, 1 and 8 are changing lines, while the others are all fixed. 2, 3, 5, and 8 are yin, whereas 1, 4, 6, and 7 are yang in nature due to the trigrams with which they are traditionally associated.

For example, if one has obtained 8 sticks from the first casting, 4 from the second, 6 from the third, 1 from the fourth, 2 from the fifth, and 1 from the last, this means the first line (8 sticks) is *tai yin* (changing yin), the second (4 sticks) is *shao yang*, the third (6) is *shao yang*, the fourth (1) *tai yang* (changing yang), the fifth (2) *shao yin*, and the sixth (1) is *tai yang* (changing yang). This process is illustrated as follows:

Remainder	Original Hexagram		New Hexagram
	50		11

1 stick (*Tai yang*)	——————o—————— 6th line	➡	————— —————
2 sticks (*Shao yin*)	————— ————— 5th line		————— —————
1 stick (*Tai yang*)	——————o—————— 4th line	➡	————— —————
6 sticks (*Shao yang*)	———————————— 3rd line		————————————
4 sticks (*Shao yang*)	———————————— 2nd line		————————————
8 sticks (*Tai yin*)	——————x—————— 1st line	➡	————————————

Ding   *Tai*
(*Ting*)   (*T'ai*)

The Simplified Method

This method works in a very similar way to the dice method. In this simplest method with the sticks, one only casts three times — the first casting to determine the upper trigram, the second for the lower trigram, and the third for the changing line.

One begins exactly the same as in the former two methods until one picks up the human stick and places it between the left little and fourth fingers. However, in this simplified method, one does not deal with the sticks that one places on their desk (earth) after the first separation. One only counts the sticks in their left hand or the heaven sticks. To determine the upper trigram, after the first dividing of the sticks, count off the remaining sticks in the left hand with the right by eights until one has 7 or less than 7 sticks. Then add the human stick to the remainder to get the final number of the sticks. If there are no sticks left after counting them off by eights, the number is 1. If there are 7, the number is 8, etc. After obtaining the number for the upper trigram, repeat the same procedure for the lower trigram.

As for the changing line, repeat the same casting procedure except count off the sticks by sixes. One will then have 5 or less than 5 sticks remaining in their left hand and 1 between the little and fourth fingers. If one has 5 sticks left,

46

add 1 human stick and get 6. This indicates that the changing line is the top line of the hexagram. If no stick remains except the human stick, this adds up to 1 which means the first line is changing. When one has gotten all three numbers, one is ready to form a hexagram with a changing line by matching these numbers with the trigrams as follows:

1	2	3	4
Qian	*Dui*	*Li*	*Zhen*
(*Ch'ien*)	(*Tui*)	(*Li*)	(*Chen*)
the Creative Heaven	the Joyous Lake	the Clinging Fire	the Arousing Thunder

5	6	7	8
Sun	*Kan*	*Gen*	*Kun*
(*Sun*)	(*K'an*)	(*Ken*)	(*K'un*)
the Gentle Wind	the Abysmal Water	the Keeping Still Mountain	the Receptive Earth

This correspondence of trigrams and numbers is exactly the same as that in the dice method. For example, if one obtains 8 (7 sticks in the left hand and 1 human stick between the little and fourth fingers) from the first casting, 4 from the second casting, and 3 from the third, the upper trigram is *Kun*, the lower trigram is *Zhen*, forming Hexagram 24, *Fu* (Return) with the third line changing. This example is illustrated as follows:

47

Remainder

24

The first casting: 8 = *Kun*

The second casting: 4 = *Zhen* ——x—— = 3 The third casting

Fu
(*Fu*)

Thus, with the third line changing from yin to yang, the original hexagram changes from Hexagram 24, *Fu* (Return) to Hexagram 36, *Ming Yi* (Darkening of the Light).

Original Hexagram   **New Hexagram**

24   36

→

Fu   *Ming Yi*
(*Fu*)   (*Ming I*)

The Computer Method

As mentioned above, there are several computer programs which randomly generate hexagrams with moving lines. If one already has a computer on their desk which is running all day, this can be a very handy way of obtaining a hexagram. In general, one first types in their question. One should pause a moment, meditating on this question, and then, when they feel they have an answer, one pushes a button and immediately a hexagram appears before one's eyes on the video display screen. Next, pushing another button, one can see how their original hexagram changes into a new or progressed hexagram. Although some may balk at using such a mechanical process for casting the *I Ching*, two things should be kept in mind. First, binary logic is the basis for modern computing. This was derived from Leibnitz's mathematics, who got the idea from the Chinese. Thus, one can say that computers operate on essentially the same symbolic language as the *I Ching*, in which case 0 and 1 become nothing other than yin and yang.

Secondly, if the mechanisms behind the oracular prognotications of the *I Ching* are none other than synchronicity and the holographic nature of reality, then pushing a computer button at a moment thus stopping a random generation of numbers is no different than throwing coins or dice. All are governed by chaos theory and the laws of probability, and all are equally valid statistically.

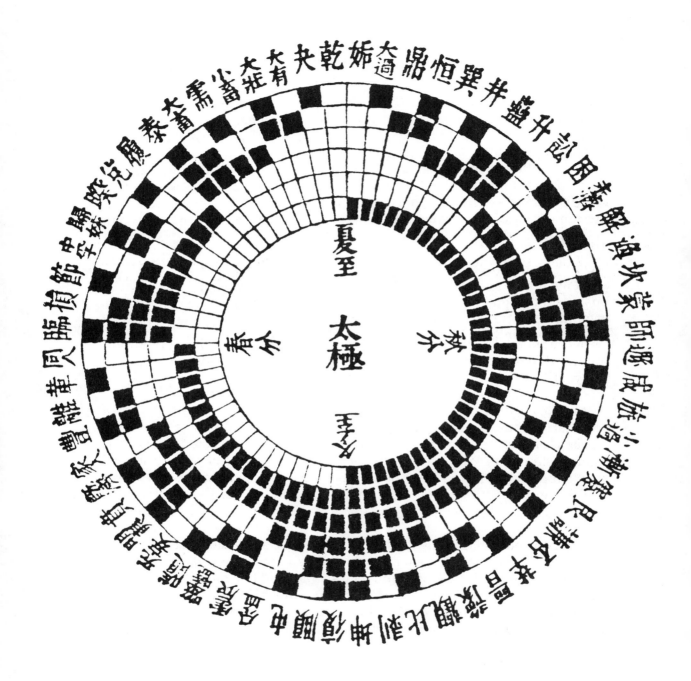

Diagram showing how *tai ji* evolves into yin & yang, the four manifestations, the eight trigrams, and ultimately the sixty-four hexagrams.

(From Zhang Jing-yue's *Lei Jing Tung Yi* [*The Systematic Classic's Illustrated Appendix*])

4

Interpreting the *I Ching*

The *I Ching* speaks to us in a symbolic language which tends to be cryptic and enigmatic. It rarely speaks to us directly and in a straightforward way. Since it was written thousands of years ago out of the deep inspiration of a highly spiritual people, it may baffle us moderns with its thick clouds of seeming obscurity. This book was so mysterious even for Confucius that he had to write his own annotations on its symbolism. In addition, historical, philosophical, and cultural differences create even further hardship for us in interpreting the *I Ching*. How can one cope with such a book?

First of all, even though interpretation of the *I Ching* is ultimately a matter of personal and individual symbolic association, one should learn how past scholars of the *I Ching* have interpreted it. Thanks to the tremendous accomplishment of Western students of this book, we now have a substantial body of books and papers on this subject in English. I have listed major works available in English in the bibliography so that one can read as much as one needs to grasp the ways the *I Ching* uses symbolism to convey its meaning.

In addition, one should also cast the *I Ching* on a regular basis on every conceivable subject in one's life into which they wish to gain spiritual insight. Every time one obtains a hexagram, they should meditate on this answer and read about it in the available *I Ching* literature. And, by all means, record your readings! The longer one practices, the deeper becomes one's understanding of *I Ching* symbolism, and there is no end to it.

It is also very helpful to learn a few basic principles of *I Ching* interpretation.

Even though there are many layers to *I Ching* imagery, there are only a few basic rules one need follow to construct a good interpretation of this symbolism. Especially, in medical divination, due to the specific scope of its objectives, these rules can be laid out in a simple, yet systematic way.

The Basic Structure of Interpretation in Medical Divination

As discussed in the preceding chapter, it is important not to ask convoluted questions. Large, multifaceted questions should be broken down into small, simple questions so that, during interpretation, one does not have to deal with the gigantic and potentially confusing job of deciphering the whole message at once. For instance, it is not prudent to ask a question like "What should I do with this patient?" because, first of all, the question is extremely vague and inexplicit in terms of its purpose. Second, it is too big a question to attack at one time. It is more productive to break this question down into a series of smaller questions each concerning the various aspects of the case about which one wants to learn. Thus, one should formulate individual questions about their patient's diagnosis, etiology, treatment plan, prognosis, etc. and then cast the *I Ching* on each of these so that it can give its opinions about the patient from many different angles. This is one of the ways to make interpretation easy and simple. In reality, after consulting the *I Ching* for a year or so, one will begin to realize that this multi-faceted approach is very systematic and works very well.

At the same time, it is very important to know the history of one's patient well when going into an interpretation in depth. As one will see below under the medical readings for each hexagram, the indications for the trigrams and hexagrams given are various, and, unless one knows the patient's history, they will have a hard time choosing the correct indications for the case at hand.

There are essentially three levels of interpretation one should progress through in medical divination. The first is the hexagram level, the second is the trigram level, and the third is the changing line level. After examining one's answer at each of these three levels individually, one can then incorporate the various aspects of symbolism inherent in these to come up with a coherent understanding of the problem in the form of a judgment or advice. Typically, each of these three respective levels gives a deeper, more detailed explanation of the situation. Thus, these three levels of informaton proceed from general to specific. However, the reader should be aware that such a synthesis is not always possible due to the complexity of the issues with which one is dealing.

Interpreting the Hexagram

First, one should look at the hexagram as a whole. The hexagram as a whole represents the generalized answer to their question. One should read the image and the judgement for the hexagram and ponder upon the nature of the central idea of the hexagram. This gives one a feeling for whether the answer is generally auspicious or inauspicious. In this book, general ideas for each hexagram are summarized under the heading "general indications" at the beginning of each hexagram.

As one becomes more familiar with the hexagrams and their structure, one can also begin seeing the patient's body symbolized in the hexagram and can begin to take into account the relative balances and imbalances of yin and yang based on such concepts of line placement as correct and incorrect placement, correspondence and annexation.

Interpreting the Trigrams

After studying the symbolic message of the hexagram as a whole, one should then go on to the second level of interpretation. This is accomplished by first taking the hexagram apart into its two component trigrams. Each of these should be looked at separately. One can separate the hexagram either into an upper trigram (lines 4, 5, and 6) and a lower trigram (lines 1, 2, and 3) or one can separate it into an upper nuclear trigram (lines 3, 4, and 5) and a lower nuclear trigram (lines 2, 3, and 4). (See Chapter 2 concerning nuclear trigrams.)

The purpose of this process is to look at deeper levels of *I Ching* symbolism than encountered in step one or at the first level of interpretation. At this level, one is able to see, for example, what is going on underneath the superficial symptomatology of the patient — what forces are operating in what fashion. Since each of the trigrams is associated with one of the five phases (at least according to post-Song Dynasty interpretation), one can often read how the lower trigram's phase is operating on the upper trigram's phase. This then gives a five phase correspondence theory picture of the disease mechanism involved.

Especially, examination of the nuclear trigrams often gives one an amazing insight into the inmost roots of a patient's problems about which the patient may have never talked during consultation. This level of interpretation also sometimes enables one to gain surprisingly deep insights into the most concealed aspect of their patient's life of which even they are not conscious!

Interpreting the Changing Lines

The third step is interpreting the changing line(s). Depending on the casting technique one uses, one can have from 0-6 changing lines. If there is no changing line, the *I Ching*'s answer tends to be quite specific and definite and the situation with which one is dealing is inclined to be fixed. In terms of medical dividination, the changing lines often speak directly about pathologic processes occuring in specific areas of the body. The more changing lines, the more changeable and fluid the circumstance. Especially in medical divination, many changing lines often indicate many rapid changes happening at multiple sites. In this kind of situation, one needs to cast the *I Ching* frequently so that one can catch up with their patient's condition. Sometimes, in the case of an very acute illness, one may want to consult the *I Ching* several times a day. On the other hand, if one is dealing with a slow, chronic illness, one may want to cast it only once a month. How often one needs to ask for help from the *I Ching* really depends upon the patient's situation.

After one has converted all the changing lines in the hexagram, one needs to go through the three levels of interpretation all over again with the new hexagram. This may sound like hard work, but it gets easier very quickly with practice. One should pay special attention to the lines that have changed during the conversion. Essentially, the new hexagram tells one a great deal about changes in the patient's condition in future, while the changing line(s) explain how and in what way these changes will take place.

Applying *I Ching* Interpretation in Clinical Practice

The easiest way of explaining how one can apply *I Ching* interpretation to their clinical practice is to give some examples. These examples will both show how interpretation is arrived at and the kind of information the *I Ching* has to offer to medical practitioners.

I once had a cancer patient with whom I worked for 9 years before she finally passed away. She was a 52 year-old Caucasian woman who originally came to see me for acupuncture treatment for back pain in 1984. I took her history in detail during the first consultation which revealed no major physical illnesses in the past. She mostly suffered from deep anxiety neurosis and periodic depression. Except for her back pain and mild fatigue, she did not have any other complaints. Examination revealed mild kidney yin weakness with slight liver qi stagnation. Her pulses were mildly sunken and wiry and her face was a bit sallow and flushed, but these signs were within normal range. Her abdomen showed slight subcostal spasm due to liver qi stagnation with some blood stasis in the lower burner. Her overall condition appeared to be healthy.

After the first session, I consulted the *I Ching* concerning her diagnosis and I obtained Hexagram 1, *Qian* (*Ch'ien*), the Creative, with the fifth line changing from yang to yin thus resulting in Hexagram 14, *Da You* (*Da Yu*), Possession in Great Measure. The following illustration shows the results of the oracle.

Original Hexagram	New Hexagram
1	14

Qian
(Ch'ien)

Da You
(Ta Yu)

I first looked at the Hexagram 1 and Hexagram 14 as wholes. As explained in Chapter 5, the general indications for Hexagram 1 are usually virulent illnesses with grave consequences which was completely opposite to what I saw in this patient. In addition, Hexagram 1 changed into Hexagram 14 which also indicated a powerful illness with great yang and heat. At this point, this reading did not make any sense to me at all.

Perplexed with the results, I ventured onto the second stage or level of interpretation which is analysis of the trigrams. The original hexagram, Hexagram 1, consists of two of the same trigrams, *Qian (Ch'ien)*, the Creative, and the its nuclear trigrams are also *Qian (Ch'ien)*, the Creative. This usually indicates severe problems of the nervous system, an extremely lethal and toxic condition, etc. The new hexagram, Hexagram 14, can be divided into two sets of trigrams, one set consisting of *Li (Li)*, Fire, and *Qian (Ch'ien)*, the Creative, and the other set (*i.e.*, the nuclear trigrams) consisting of *Dui (Tui)*, the Joyous, and *Qian (Ch'ien)*, the Creative. Trigram *Qian* again strongly suggested that the patient was in a serious condition, while the trigram *Dui (Tui)*, the Joyous, indicated problems of the digestive system, female system, toxins, etc.

Although these findings made me more confused, I continued onto the third step, the analysis of the changing lines. In this particular case, there was only one line changing, from yang to yin at the fifth position. This usually denotes that there is a change of yang nature occurring in the chest which will change in future to a yin condition.

After putting all these pieces of information together, it seemed to me that the *I Ching* was telling me that, even though the patient appeared to be healthy, she must be suffering from a serious hidden condition in her chest. I knew that she had problems in her nervous system and that was not new to me. I also thought that it was indicating that she was toxic and she had problems in her female organs and digestive system.

Based on these findings, I referred her to one of my associate physicians for consultation a week after her initial consultation with me. I did not tell my patient anything about my *I Ching* divination but just told her that I wanted medical clearance since she had not had an examination for a long time. The patient reluctantly went to the doctor, and, to my greatest surprise, the doctor found a lump in her right breast, which, later on, was confirmed by biopsy to be malignant! This was what the *I Ching* was talking about, I thought. The doctor immediately suggested total mastectomy, but the patient refused the operation because she was extremely scared and paranoid about it.

At this point, I consulted the *I Ching* again. My question was, "Should she have the operation?", and I obtained Hexagram 18, *Gu (Ku)*, Work On What Has Been Spoiled, with no changing line. This hexagram is a symbol of chronic illness and the repair work on what has been damaged. I felt that the *I Ching* was definitely approving the operation and, therefore, I told my patient to go ahead with the surgery. After a long discussion, the patient hesitantly agreed and I sent her to a surgeon friend of mine for mastectomy. The operation was performed uneventfully, but the doctor said that the cancer had metastasized to other parts of her body and the patient had at most two years to live even after chemotherapy and radiation.

The patient was so fearful of those conventional therapies that she returned to see me for post-operative treatments. I then made an agreement with her that an oncologist, also a friend of mine, and I would take care of her provided that she would see him every three months. She also signed an affidavit under oath that she knew that I was not treating her for cancer but was simply helping her immune system to work better. The oncologist also told me that he might be able to help her, but he was not sure whether or not chemotherapy would be really helpful in her particular case. At any rate, I cast the *I Ching* again to know what was going on with her condition, and I obtained Hexagram 22, *Bi (Pi)*, Grace, with the 1st and the 3rd lines changing, which converts to Hexagram 23, *Bo (Po)*, Splitting Apart.

Original Hexagram	New Hexagram
22	23
Bi	*Bo*
(Pi)	*(Po)*

This was the message from the *I Ching* about the patient's condition right after surgery. Hexagram 22, Grace, in general suggests that superficial symptoms did not necessarily reflect her internal conditions. As a matter of fact, in spite of the strains from the operation, the patient did not look at all bad. However, the *I Ching* was suggesting that there were changes happening in her system (changing lines), and Hexagram 22, *Bo* (*Po*), Splitting Apart, also indicated that the patient had a chronic hot condition or chronic spleen disease.

I then took the hexagrams apart into upper and lower and nuclear trigrams and also formed the nuclear hexagram. Below is how it came out.

Original Hexagram	Upper Trigram	Lower Trigram	Upper Nuclear Trigram	Lower Nuclear Trigram	Nuclear Hexagram
Bi	*Gen*	*Li*	*Zhen*	*Kan*	*Jie*
(Pi)	*(Ken)*	*(Li)*	*(Chen)*	*(K'an)*	*(Hsieh)*

After analyzing the upper trigram and the lower trigram of the original hexagram, I learned that the upper part of the patient's body (represented by the upper trigram) was stable (*Gen* = Mountain, Keeping Still), but the lower part (lower trigram) of the body was changing from *Li* (Fire) to *Kun* (Earth) by the 1st and the 3rd lines changing. This means that a hot condition (fire) in the lower body was changing to a chronic condition of congestion (earth). At the same time, based on the nuclear trigrams, I could guess that there were some pains (*Zhen*) in her upper body (upper trigram) and toxins or blood stasis (*Kan*) in her lower body (lower trigram) as deep pathology. Finally, I looked at the nuclear hexagram, Hexagram 40, *Jie* (*Hsieh*), Deliverance, which indicated that the patient needed dispersion of internal toxins and release of obstruction or blockage. The analysis of the nuclear trigrams and the nuclear hexagram gave a great deal of information about what should be done with the patient later.

I also examined the changed or progressed hexagram, Hexagram 23, *Bo* (*Po*), Splitting Apart. As a whole, Hexagram 23 indicates general degeneration, weakness of qi and blood, and possible death of the patient. I knew that this was a strong warning from the *I Ching* that she would eventually die from the cancer. However, since the changing lines were line 1 and 3, I figured that she was still at the early stage of the illness.

With all this information from the *I Ching*, I began treating her. I first put her through a cleansing process (as suggested by the *I Ching*) by giving her various herbal formulas. I cast the *I Ching* by the dice technique for changing her herbs and acupuncture every week. What I did was to come up with a few formulas based on the weekly examination and consulted the *I Ching* for final selection. Since I need to do this process very quickly on many patients every day, I frequently use the dice casting method.

After a month of herbal and acupuncture treatment every other day, she became stronger by the week. We then cut down on the treatment to twice a week, and continued the schedule for nine years until she passed away. Even though she was full of cancer all over her body, she had no pain until one month before her death. This, I believe, was because, during the years that I treated her, I consulted the *I Ching* weekly and managed to control her pains.

At the same time, I realized that I tended to obtain Hexagram 23, *Bo* (*Po*), Splitting Apart, over and over again for this patient. The amazing thing was that, as she came closer and closer to her death, the changing lines in the hexagram also slowly moved up to the top line! And, when I obtained the same hexagram without any changing lines, I knew that the *I Ching* was definitely telling me that it was time for her to go. I arranged everything for her through a hospice and, sure enough, she passed away very peacefully a month later.

When one consults the *I Ching* on a same patient for years like I did, one comes to realize that there is always one hexagram, like Hexagram 23 for this lady, which tends to come up over and over again. I call it an archetype hexagram which symbolizes the soul of the person. When one finds such an archetype hexagram, one should study all the symbolism of that particular hexagram very thoroughly because you one can then learn a lot about that person. For example, I have a patient whose archetype hexagram turned out to be 56, *Lu* (*Lu*), the Wanderer. This is an American man who lives in India. He has been seeing me for one month out of every year for the last 10 years. He is a musician and he is also a perpetual traveller. It is also interesting to know that Hexagram 56 generally indicates contagious illnesses of migrating nature and this man has come to see me every year with some kind of infection!

Specifics to Keep in Mind in Medical Divination

There are several readings of particular importance in traditional medical divination. First of all, if one obtains a hexagram composed of two trigrams of the same element, like Hexagram 29, *Kan* (*K'an*), the Abysmal, as an original hexagram or a changed hexagram in diagnosis and prognosis for one's patient, it often indicates a serious condition. Therefore, when one gets such a hexagram, although the patient may look healthy, one should look deeper into the situation of that patient. I personally have obtained such a hexagram for some of my patients and it has often turned out that the patient had, for example, occult malignancy.

It is also traditionally said to be sinister and ominous to obtain Hexagram 7, *Shi*

(*Shih*), The Army, Hexagram 12, *Pi* (*P'i*), Standstill, Hexagram 16, *Yu* (*Yu*), Enthusiasm, Hexagram 45, *Cui* (*Ts'ui*), Gathering Together, Hexagram 62, *Xiao Guo* (*Hsiao Kuo*), Preponderance of the Small, because the shapes of these hexagrams intimate tombstones in Oriental iconography. Especially, in the case of seriously sick patients, these hexagrams may suggest that the patient is in their terminal stage.

Another group of hexagrams of possibly grave consequences are Hexagram 18, *Gu* (*Ku*), Work on What Has Been Spoiled, Hexagram 23, *Bo* (*Po*), Splitting Apart, Hexagram 28, *Da Guo* (*Ta Kuo*), Preponderance of the Great, Hexagram 33, *Dun* (*Tun*), Retreat, Hexagram 36, *Ming Yi* (*Ming I*), Darkening of the Light, Hexagram 38, *Kui* (*K'uei*), Opposition, Hexagram 43, *Guai* (*Kuai*), Breakthrough, and Hexagram 49, *Ge* (*Ko*), Revolution. Although the indications of each of these hexagrams are different, they all suggest possible exacerbation of the condition. However, in interpreting these hexagrams, one should not be too rigid but allow oneself to be flexible and to put everything into consideration to work for the best interest of their patient.

Some hexagrams strongly indicate diseases of sexual origin. They are Hexagram 11, *Tai* (*T'ai*), Peace, Hexagram 18, Work on what Has Been Spoiled, Hexagram 31, *Xian* (*Hsien*), Influence, and Hexagram 54, *Gui Mei* (*Kuei Mei*), The Marrying Maiden. Patients for whom one casts these hexagrams tend to hide their history of venereal diseases, such as AIDS. Therefore, one must pay attention to that aspect of their life when if one obtains one of these hexagrams.

One time, about ten years ago, I had a 65 year old Mexican patient who presented with multiple joint pains of unknown etiology. She had seen many physicians, but they could not really help her. I consulted the *I Ching* and obtained Hexagram 31, *Xian* (*Hsien*), Influence, with the fourth line changing. Since this generally indicates illnesses of sexual origin, I ran a blood test on her, and it turned out that she was highly positive with syphilis! I had to send this patient to the county health department for treatment. She later told me that she had been raped when she was young. The *I Ching* was telling me that she was suffering from tertiary syphilis. This is just one of many amazing cases of hidden venereal diseases that I have discovered through the *I Ching*.

These examples give some indication of how I use the *I Ching* in my clinical practice and also how a *I Ching* hexagram can be cast and interpreted medically.

5

Medical Readings for the 64 Hexagrams

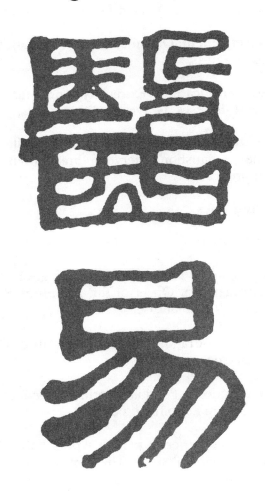

1. *Qian (Ch'ien)*, **The Creative**

The movement of heaven is powerful.
Thus the superior person keeps improving himself.

The Judgement: *Qian* means great success. Perseverance brings good progress.

General Indications: Extremely yang conditions. Very acute and virulent illnesses. Grave conditions.

Specific Indications: Contagious febrile diseases. Extreme mental exhaustion. Nervous breakdown. Terminal illnesses including cancer.

Moving lines

Line 1: The dragon is hiding. Do not act.

Fair prognosis. Patient not ready to get better. May get worse. Severe diarrhea. Onset of flu. Apoplexy. Stroke. Spontaneous abortion. Venereal diseases.

Line 2: The dragon appears in the field. One should see the great person.

Poor prognosis. Possible death. Contagious disease with high fever. Severe abdominal pain.

Line 3: The superior person works hard all day long. In the evening, they still strive. There may be danger, but there is no fault in it.

Fair prognosis. Status quo. No effects from medicine. Respiratory illnesses with chills, phlegm, and fever. Back pain with coldness.

Line 4: Wavering flight of the dragon over the depths. There is no fault in it.

Fair prognosis. Alternating symptoms. Slow recovery. Illness may recur. Chest and abdominal pain with fever.

Line 5: The dragon soars in the heavens. One should see the great person.

Poor prognosis. Peak of disease. Dangerous. Great fever with thirst, headaches, or bleeding.

Line 6: The arrogant dragon regrets his action.

Extremely poor prognosis. Very grave conditions. Unconsciousness. Severe headaches. Utmost mental confusion.

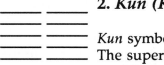

2. *Kun (K'un)*, The Receptive

Kun symbolizes the strength of the earth.
The superior person, thus, benefits the world
   with their merits.

The Judgement: *Kun* means great success. Improvement through the firmness of a mare. The superior person has a place to go. If one tries to go ahead, one goes astray. If one follows, one will find a master. One should find friends in the west and south. Even if friends are lost in the east and north, calm perseverance will bring good fortune.

General Indications: Extremely yin conditions. Lack of *yuan qi*. Poor ability to recover. Slow movement of illness. Grave conditions.

Specific Indications: Spleen and stomach disorders causing mental and physical weakness. Weak limbs. Poor digestion. Diarrhea. Vomiting. Cold constitution.

Moving lines

Line 1: Treading on hoarfrost leads to solid ice.

Usually fair prognosis. Gradual exacerbation. Quick treatment is imperative or poor prognosis. Possible recurrence. Constipation due to spleen vacuity. Weak lower extremities. Deficiency of *yuan qi*.

Line 2: Straight, square, great. Everything improves without effort.

Fair prognosis. Slow recovery. Possible danger of exacerbation. Abdominal pain. Blood stasis in the abdomen. Damp heat in the

66

spleen. Premature delivery.

Line 3: Hide your talent. Continue to persevere, or the imperial service will end in vain.

Fair prognosis. Tendency to become chronic. Slow and poor recovery. Lower back pain. Food stagnation in the abdomen. Spleen qi vacuity.

Line 4: A tied-sack. No blame. No praise.

Fair prognosis. Danger. Needs rest for a long time. Abdominal problems. Poor appetite. Indigestion. Blood vacuity causing mental weakness.

Line 5: A yellow skirt. Great success.

Poor prognosis. Needs immediate care. Chest problem. Tumor in the chest and shoulder area. Tuberculosis. Pneumonia.

Line 6: The dragon flies in the field. His blood is black and yellow.

Grave prognosis. Possible death. Brain tumor with vertigo. Paralysis due to stroke or tetanus. Mental derangement.

3. *Zhun (Chun)*, **Difficulty at the Beginning**

Clouds over thunder.
The image of *Zhun*.
Thus the superior person establishes the order.

The Judgement: *Zhun* means great success. Perseverance brings good progress. Nothing should be undertaken. One should obtain helpers.

General Indications: At the beginning of an illness. Unclear prognosis. Symptoms severe at onset. May become chronic.

Specific Indications: Cold and dampness in the spleen. Food stagnation. Retention of urine. Muscle spasms due to the wind.

Moving lines

Line 1: Hesitation and distress. Perseverance brings good fortune. One should obtain helpers.

Fair prognosis if treated consistently. Needs conservative treatment. No drastic measures should be taken. Cold damp conditions. Cold and weak lower extremities. Disharmony between the spleen and stomach.

Line 2: Difficulties and obstacles. Horse and wagon split. One wants to marry the maiden. She is chaste. She does not marry him. Ten years later, she gets married.

Chronic digestive problem due to spleen vacuity. Proper diet imperative. Otherwise, poor prognosis.

Line 3: The deer hunter without a forester loses his way in the forest. The superior person thus, abandons their game. To go on leads to humiliation.

Slow recovery. Misdiagnosed and needs second opinion. Fever and chills. Constipation due to heat in intestines. Muscle spasms. Internal bleeding.

Line 4: The horse and wagon split. She wants to get married. To go on brings good fortune. Perseverance brings misfortune.

Over the peak. Fair recovery. Flushing-up of liver wind. Tinnitus. Gum problems. Spasms.

Line 5: Difficulties in blessing. Moderate perseverance brings good fortune. Great perseverance leads to misfortune.

Temporary aggravation but good recovery. May recur later. Malnutrition. Night sweats due to yin vacuity. Blood stasis in the chest. Fatigue.

Line 6: Horse and wagon split. Bloody tears will be shed.

Peak of an illness with great pain, but may turn for the better suddenly. Severe brain dysfunction. Headaches. Mental anguish. Eye infection.

4. *Meng (Mêng),* Youthful Folly

There is a spring at the foot of the mountain.
The image of *Meng.*
Thus the superior person realizes themself
    and cultivates their character.

The Judgement: *Meng* means success. It is not I who seek the young fool. It is the young fool who seeks me. I instruct him at the first oracle. If he asks two or three times, he is unreasonable and I will not give him any more advice. Perseverance brings good progress.

General Indications: Danger of misdiagnosis. May need a second opinion. Medicine may not work. Tendency to become chronic.

Specific Indications: Spleen vacuity causing food stagnation, diarrhea, back pain, loss of energy, general toxic state. Latent heat. Blood stasis.

Moving lines

Line 1: To develop a fool, one should use discipline. The fetters should be detached. To continue this way will lead to misfortune.

Fair prognosis. Tendency to become a chronic problem. Pain in foot. Cold lower extremities. Diarrhea with blood and pus.

Line 2: If one can tolerate the fool, good fortune will come. To know how to woo a woman brings good fortune. The son will be cable of taking care of the family.

70

Fair prognosis, but there may be sudden exacerbation. Lower abdominal problem with heat and food stagnation.

Line 3: Do not marry a woman who loses control of herself over a wealthy man. Nothing is advantageous in it.

Poor prognosis with tendency to become chronic. *Jing* essence vacuity. Back pain. Melancholy. Fatigue. Constipation. Dysuria.

Line 4: The fool suffers from ignorance. Humiliation.

Poor prognosis. Spleen vacuity causing emotional problems. Subcostal spasms with liver wind.

Line 5: Child-like ignorance brings good fortune.

Good recovery. Seek a good physician. Cold in the chest with fever and chills.

Line 6: One should not commit offense while correcting ignorance. Only prevention can rectify it.

Good prognosis if treated at the beginning of illness. Otherwise, poor outlook. Headaches. Generalized edema. Boils on the head.

5. *Xu (Hsü)*, Waiting (Nourishment)

Clouds climb in the sky.
The image of *Xu.*
The superior person thus cheerfully
    eats and drinks in celebration.

The Judgement: *Xu* means sincerity. Great success. Perseverance brings good fortune. One should cross the great river.

General Indications: The illness should not be treated in a hurry without careful examination and diagnosis or it could easily get worse. Wait and look into the root of it cautiously. Possibly fatal conditions.

Specific Indications: Phlegm stagnation in various parts of the body causing vomiting, constipation, lung congestion, food stagnation, and a general toxic state. Coma. Death.

Moving lines

Line 1: Waiting in the meadows, one should be consistent. There is no fault in this.

At the beginning of an illness. May prolong if not treated properly now. Gait problem. Boils in the lower extremities. Leg cramps.

Line 2: Waiting at the waterfront, there is some gossip about one, but there will be success in the end.

Chronic illnesses with poor prognosis. External cold with internal heat. Bladder trouble. Flushing up with thirst. Sexual excess.

Line 3: Waiting in the mud, the enemy arrives.

Poor prognosis. Phlegm in the intestines causing abdominal distention, and subcostal spasm. Bone fracture. Joint disorders.

Line 4: Waiting in blood, one should escape from the pit.

Serious condition but good prognosis with radical treatment. Various chest conditions. Phlegm due to faulty spleen function with nausea and vomiting. Acute febrile illnesses. Bleeding disorders.

Line 5: Waiting with wine and food, perseverance brings good fortune.

Good outlook. Danger of recurrence. Phlegm in the lungs causing tightness and pressure in the chest. Diarrhea with pus and blood.

Line 6: Having fallen into the pit, three uninvited guests arrive. Honoring them brings good fortune in the end.

Fair prognosis. Chronic qi stagnation. Chest congestion with phlegm. Depression and melancholy. Menstrual difficulties from qi stagnation.

6. *Song (Sung),* Conflict

Heaven and water go their opposite ways.
The image of *Song.*
The superior person thus examines their strategy
  in the beginning.

The Judgement: *Song* means that one is innocent though accused. To halt halfway brings good fortune. To go all the way brings misfortune. One should see the great person. One should cross the great river.

General Indications: Yin/yang disharmony. Contradictory symptoms. Disharmony of the qi and blood. Chronic imbalances leading to death.

Specific Indications: Painful spasms of the chest and abdomen due to disharmony among many elements. Prostration with mental and emotional conflicts. Toxins causing diarrhea and hemorrhoids. Excessive menstruation.

Moving lines

Line 1: If one does not prolong the affair, although there is a little gossip, one will have good fortune in the end.

Good prognosis. Joint pain in the extremities due to stagnation of cold. Paralysis of the legs.

Line 2: Not being able to overcome the conflict, one escapes and returns to their village of three hundred households. They remain free of damage.

Good recovery. Accumulation of various toxins in the lower abdomen causing damage to the rest of the body.

74

Line 3: One still earns their living under their former king. Perseverance may be dangerous, but, in the end, it brings success. In the service of one's lord, one cannot accomplish any work.

Occasional exacerbation but good prognosis. Gastrointestinal infections. Abdominal distention due to dampness.

Line 4: Not being able to overcome the conflict, one returns to the order of one's lord. If they thus change their attitude and stay peaceful and firm, they will have good fortune.

Fair prognosis. Needs rest to prevent recurrence of illness. Food stagnation. Intestinal parasites. Mild cold. Moderate wind diseases.

Line 5: To engage in conflict brings supreme good fortune.

Excellent prognosis. Chronic heat stagnation. Flushing-up. Persistent fever. Headaches.

Line 6: Even if one is awarded a leather belt, by the end of the morning, it will have been snatched away three times.

May improve a bit but poor prognosis in the end. Phlegm in the lungs. Mental derangement. Severe *jing* essence vacuity. Neck problem. Night sweats. Kidney vacuity in the elderly.

7. *Shi (Shih)*, The Army

Water under the earth.
The image of *Shi*.
The superior person is generous to the people
  and thus takes good care of them.

The Judgement: *Shi* means perseverance. Great persons have good fortune. There is no fault in this.

General Indications: Acute and virulent diseases which require immediate attention. Vigorous treatment necessary to avoid grave consequences. Death.

Specific Indications: Diseases caused by kidney and spleen vacuity. Food stagnation causing poisoning with pain. Acute nephritis. Pancreatitis. Venereal diseases. Menstrual problems.

Moving lines

Line 1: An army must be dispatched in proper order or there will be misfortune.

Good prognosis if treated immediately or may lead to serious end. Painful cold lower extremities. Food stagnation causing constipation. Dysmenorrhea.

Line 2: One is in the midst of the army. This is good fortune. There is no fault in it. The king bestowed order three times.

Fair prognosis. Damp heat in the spleen. Food poisoning. Contagious abdominal diseases. Excessive menstrual bleeding.

Line 3: The army carries corpses in wagons. There will be misfortune.

76

Poor prognosis. Possibly fatal. Bleeding disorders. Severe pain and swelling of lower back. Toxemia of pregnancy. Breech birth.

Line 4: The army retreats. There is no fault in this.

Good prognosis if treated immediately. Otherwise, poor outlook. Obstructive kidney or liver disease. Beginnings of cancer. Possible miscarriage.

Line 5: There is game in the field. To strike it brings good fortune. There is no fault in this.

The eldest son leads the army. The younger son carries corpses in wagons. Perseverance brings misfortune.

Poor prognosis. Pulmonary disease. Severe diarrhea with blood and pus. Profound yin vacuity with profuse night sweats.

Line 6: The great king issues commands, founds states, and grants families with fiefs. One should not employ inferior persons.

Fair prognosis. Vertigo. Headaches. Tinnitus. Spleen qi vacuity. General toxic state.

8. *Bi (Pi)*, Holding Together (Union)

Water on the earth.
The image of *Bi*.
Thus the ancient kings bestowed states as fiefs
   and established cordial alliance with the feudal lords.

The Judgement: *Bi* means good fortune. Consult the oracle. If one is honorable, consistent, and firm, there is no blame. Those who are uncertain quickly arrive. Those who come too late meet with misfortune.

General Indications: Kidney and spleen vacuity. Weak constitution. Prone to illness. Chronic tendency. Possible death.

Specific Indications: Chest problems. Weak stomach. Indigestion. Diarrhea. Food stagnation. Ear problem. Kidney diseases.

Moving lines

Line 1: A sincere union. There is no fault in it. The chalice is full of sincerity. Thus good fortune comes from others in the end.

Fair prognosis. The problem may get better temporarily but worsen later if the patient does not get enough rest. Problems with lower extremities. Diarrhea with pain.

Line 2: Internal union. Perseverance brings good fortune.

Fair prognosis. Bleeding. Food poisoning. Kidney dysfunction. Chills.

Line 3: Union with the wrong people.

78

Poor prognosis. Lower abdominal congestion with pain. Lower back pain leading to paralysis.

Line 4: Union with others. Perseverance brings good fortune.

Fair prognosis. Change physician. Food and phlegm stagnation. Abdominal toxins.

Line 5: A fair union. In the chase, the king only uses beaters on three sides and forgoes game through the front. The villagers do not punish it. There will be good fortune.

Poor prognosis. Severe chest problem with pain. Vomiting leading to extreme yin exhaustion.

Line 6: Union without a leader. There will be misfortune.

Poor prognosis. Profound exhaustion. Brain dysfunction.

9. *Xiao Xu (Hsiao Ch'u)*, The Taming Power of the Small

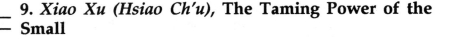

Wind blows across heaven.
The image of *Xiao Xu*.
The superior person thus cultivates
  the arts and virtues.

The Judgement: *Xiao Xu* means success. There are dense clouds but no rain comes from our western region.

General Indications: Chronic illnesses with various stagnations. Toxic conditions. Slow recovery. Beginnings of cancer.

Specific Indications: Qi and blood stagnation leading to exhaustion and depression. Phlegm stagnation causing internal heat and lung problems. Food stagnation causing constipation and gastrointestinal tumors.

Moving lines

Line 1: One returns to the right way. How can there be blame in this? There will be good fortune.

Good prognosis. Mild stagnation of cold and damp toxins in the legs. Weakness and swelling of lower extremities.

Line 2: One calmly returns. Good fortune.

Good recovery. High fever which exhausts the heart. Heat in the lower abdomen causing constipation or dark red urine.

Line 3: The wagon wheels split. Man and wife roll their eyes.

80

Good prognosis if treated by competent practitioner or poor course of recovery. Persistent internal heat and surface cold leading to liver and kidney vacuity. Lower back pain.

Line 4: If one is sincere, the blood will vanish and fear will disappear. There is no fault in this.

Good prognosis. Blood stasis with toxins. Intermittent fever and chills.

Line 5: If one is sincere and loyal, one is with their neighbors.

Good prognosis but slow recovery. Illness of the chest from various stagnations. Upper back and shoulder spasm.

Line 6: The rain has already come and it is gone now. This suggests the lasting effects of virtue. Perseverance brings the woman into danger. The moon is nearly full. To go on will bring the superior person misfortune.

Slow course of illness but good prognosis. Brain and nervous system disorder due to heat stagnation. Bleeding illness. Vomiting of blood.

10. *Lŭ (Lü)*, Treading (Conduct)

Heaven over marsh,
The image of *Lŭ*.
The superior person thus distinguishes between
    high and the low
And stabilizes peoples' minds.

The Judgement: *Lŭ* means treading on the tiger's tail. It does not bite one. There will be success.

General Indications: Qi vacuity conditions. Illnesses from damp heat. Sudden changes during the course of illness. Sudden recovery. Sudden death.

Specific Indications: Respiratory illnesses due to qi vacuity. Mental depression from qi stagnation. Damp heat leading to toxic conditions such as constipation.

Moving lines

Line 1: Simple conduct. There is progress without blame.

Good prognosis. Cold extremities with pain. Foot problems. Diarrhea. Sore throat. Onset of cold.

Line 2: Treading the level path. The perseverance of the hermit brings good fortune.

Good prognosis. Chest or abdominal pain with fever and liver wind. Palpitations with internal heat.

Line 3: If a cross-eyed man tries to see and a lame man tries to walk, they will tread on the tiger's tail and the tiger will bite them. Misfortune. The warrior, therefore, should behave like a great lord.

Fair prognosis. Blood stasis in the abdomen. Lower back pain. Toxic state due to blood and fluid stagnation. Boils all over the body. Aphasia. Inability to eat. Swelling of the vulva. Clots in the menstruate.

Line 4: One treads on the tiger's tail, but their caution and discretion brings good fortune in the end.

Fair prognosis. Wind diseases of the chest. Slow recovery. Viral bronchitis. Viral pneumonia with fever. Palpitation from heat stagnation. Damp heat in the spleen.

Line 5: Determined conduct. One should persevere with awareness of danger.

Fair prognosis. High recurrent fever. Heat in the chest and abdomen. Severe chest pains. Inability to eat. Disharmony of the qi and blood. Swelling of the neck. Poor eyesight. May require a second opinion. Possibility of wrong prescription or treatment.

Line 6: Examine your conduct and reflect on the auspicious signs. When everything is correct, one will have good fortune.

Fair prognosis. Phlegm stagnation in the chest causing difficulty of breathing. Asthma. Phlegm misting the portals of the heart. Confused state of consciousness. Food poisoning.

11. *Tai (T'ai)*, Peace

Heaven and earth unite,
The image of *Tai*.
The ruler fulfills the paths of heaven and earth
   and thus promotes gifts to help the people.

The Judgement: *Tai* means that the small goes and the great comes. There will be good fortune. It will lead to success.

General Indications: Union of yin and yang. State of perfect health. Changing lines signify deviation from healthy state.

Specific Indications: Diseases from sexual origin. Genetic illnesses. Inherited weakness in the family. Mass in the abdomen. Head sores. Amenorrhoea.

Moving lines

Line 1: When ribbon grass is pulled up, the sod comes with it. Like gathers like. To go on brings good fortune.

Good prognosis. Pain and spasms of the legs. Flushing-up of heat. Vomiting. Diarrhea. Hysteria. Influenza.

Line 2: One patiently tolerates the waste land. One crosses the river on foot with determination. One acknowledges the distant people. One disregards companions. Thus one should be able to walk on the middle path.

Fair prognosis. Fever. Phlegm with blood. Scarring of wound. Lower back pain with swelling. Failing eyesight.

Line 3: No plain not followed by a slope. No going not followed by a return. One who stays firm in adversity is no one to blame.

One must not ignore this truth. Enjoy the good fortune while one still has it.

Fair prognosis. Sharp pain in the lower back. Emotional stress on the heart. Dysentery. Palpitations. Cough with phlegm. Back pain from coldness. Syphilitic ailments.

Line 4: One lowers themself, without boasting of their wealth, to the level of their neighbors. Be genuine and sincere.

Fair prognosis. Seizures due to liver wind. Spasms of stomach or uterus. Hysteria.

Line 5: The Emperor Yi bestowed his daughter in marriage. This brings blessing and great good fortune.

Fair prognosis. Food poisoning with vomiting and diarrhea. Bleeding with pus. Cold in the intestines.

Line 6: The castle walls fall into the moat. Do not use the army. Announce your commands throughout the village. Perseverance brings misfortune.

Poor prognosis. Headaches. Brain disorders. Poor appetite. Paralysis of the extremities.

12. *Pi (P'i)*, Standstill (Stagnation)

Heaven and earth do not unite,
The image of *Pi*.
The superior person thus maintains their virtue to avoid adversity.
They do not allow themself to be honored.

The Judgement: *Pi* means immoral people. They do not benefit the superior person. The great goes and the small comes.

General Indications: Stagnation of qi and blood. Separation of yin and yang. *Zang fu* disharmony. Deep and chronic causes of illness. Very slow recovery. Blockage of internal organs.

Specific Indications: Poor circulation. Mental/emotional depression. Constipation. Food stagnation. Exhaustion. Headaches. Flushing-up of qi. Gastrointestinal tumors. Dysmenorrhea.

Moving lines

Line 1: When ribbon grass is pulled up, the sod comes with it. Like gathers like. To go on leads to good fortune. There will be success.

Good prognosis. Slow recovery. Foot ailments due to stagnation. Infantile neurosis.

Line 2: Go with the flow of things. There will be good fortune for the small. The great are blocked but they will succeed.

Fair prognosis. Abdominal pain. Diarrhea. Damp heat in the intestines. Internal heat without chills.

Line 3: One should cover their shame.

Fair prognosis. Chronic problem. Problems of the extremities. Lower back pain causing difficulty in walking. Skin infection with induration. Paralysis of the elderly. Diseases of which one may be ashamed.

Line 4: One who follows the command remains blameless. Those of like mind share the blessing.

Fair prognosis. Qi stagnation in the chest causing pain. Diseases of the nose. Bone fracture. Arthritis. Difficulty of breathing. Poor digestion due to spleen and stomach vacuity and weakness. Danger of recurrence.

Line 5: The standstill at rest. There will be good fortune for the great person. They say, "It is failing! It is failing!" One should hold onto the mulberry shoots.

Fair prognosis. Heat stagnation in the lungs and spleen. Eye diseases. Flushing-up of qi. Contagious infections of gastrointestinal tract. Danger of recurrence.

Line 6: The standstill at its end. First, it is standstill, then there is joy.

Good prognosis. Head congestion. Depression. Lack of appetite due to stomach qi vacuity. Food stagnation leading to nausea and vomiting. Danger of recurrence.

13. *Tong Ren (T'ung Jên)*, Fellowship with Men

Fire in the heaven,
The image of *Tong Ren*.
Thus the superior person organizes the clan
  and discriminates between things.

The Judgement: *Tong Ren* means fellowship with those in the field. There will be success. One should cross the great river. One should see the superior person.

General Indications: Contagious diseases. Inherited proclivity toward certain illnesses in the family. Illnesses caused by heat. Public health problems. Epidemics. Fast movement of illness. Mental function hyperactive. Death.

Specific Indications: Infectious diseases with fever. Eye infections. Mental exhaustion due to stress. Palpitations.

Moving lines

Line 1: Fellowship with those at the gate. There is no fault in this.

Fair prognosis. Contagious illness causing paralysis of lower extremities. Polio. Inability to walk. Arthritis of the legs. Influenza. Agoraphobia.

Line 2: Fellowship with those in the clan. There will be humiliation.

Poor prognosis. Possible death. Inherited diseases of the family. Contagious respiratory illnesses with fever. Constipation due to heat in the intestines.

88

Line 3: One hides their soldiers in the thicket and climbs the high hill. For three years, one will not rise.

Fair prognosis. Contagious diseases with a long incubation period. Paralysis and spasm of the lower back. Spastic pains of neck. High fever. Liver wind rising. Hysteria.

Line 4: One climbs up on the wall but one cannot attack. There will be good fortune.

Good prognosis. Contagious disease at the point of becoming symptomatic. Damp heat in the spleen. Joint pain from stagnant heat. Irregular menstruation due to heat.

Line 5: Those of the fellowship wail first and laugh later. The great army manages to meet together.

Fair prognosis. Onset of a contagious disease. Damp hot phlegm in the lungs causing difficulty in breathing. Eye infections. Heart problems due to heat. Illness due to improper diet. Infections of the heart.

Line 6: Fellowship with those in the meadows. There is no regret.

Fair prognosis. End of an infectious illness. Mental exhaustion. Meningitis. Nausea. Vomiting. Depression in the elderly.

14. *Da You (Ta Yu)*, Possession in Great Measure

Fire in heaven,
The image of *Da You*.
The superior person thus curbs evil and promotes good.
Thereby they obey the will of heaven.

The Judgement: *Da You* means supreme success.

General Indications: Heat stagnation causing fever. Yang repletion and yin vacuity. Exhaustion of fluids. Rapid change in disease picture. Two concurrent pathologies. Possible death.

Specific Indications: Diseases with high fever causing yin vacuity. Respiratory illnesses with fever and phlegm. Constipation causing toxic conditions. Brain degeneration.

Moving lines

Line 1: No association with evil. There is no fault in this. Beware of adversity. There is no blame.

Good prognosis. The illness may require a second opinion. Arthritis of the legs. Onset of cold with fever. Diarrhea. Toxic conditions with heat accumulation in the interior.

Line 2: A great wagon to load. It is good to have a place to go. There is no fault in this.

Good prognosis. Infections with high fever and mental confusion. Bleeding. Dysentery with fever and diarrhea. Illnesses due to over-indulgence.

Line 3: The prince offers service to the emperor. The small cannot do this.

Fair prognosis. Respiratory illness with chills, fever and phlegm. Menstrual problem from qi and blood disharmony. Skin irritation. Lower back pain. Boils. Sexual dysfunction.

Line 4: One makes the distinction between themself and their neighbors. There is no fault in this.

Fair prognosis. Respiratory illness with fever. Chest pains. Upper back pain. Menstrual irregularity due to toxins. Toxic conditions of the liver.

Line 5: One's inner truth is friendly yet dignified. There is good fortune.

Poor prognosis. Extremely yang conditions. Very virulent illnesses. Cancers. Respiratory infections. Severe headaches. Poor eyesight. Possible death.

Line 6: One is blessed by heaven. There is good fortune. There is nothing that does not improve.

Poor prognosis. Very active malignant illnesses. Brain infections. Mental derangement. Exhaustion.

15. *Qian (Ch'ien)*, **Modesty**

A mountain in the earth,
The image of *Qian*.
The superior person thus reduces what is too much,
  and expands what is too little.
They weigh matters
  and make them equal.

The Judgement: *Qian* means success. The superior person works things through.

General Indications: Slow-moving, chronic illnesses. Qi vacuity or stagnation leading to mental and emotional depression. Death.

Specific Indications: Fatigue of the whole body due to the spleen vacuity. Melancholy. Food stagnation and indigestion. Toxic states. Constant lower back pain. Paralysis. Cancer of gastrointestinal tract. Venereal diseases. Tardy menses.

Moving lines

Line 1: Modesty of modesty. The superior person thus crosses the great river. There is good fortune.

Good prognosis. Migrating pains in the legs due to inflammatory illnesses. Heat stagnation in the lower extremities. Feverish diseases of infants. Mumps. Toxemia of pregnancy.

Line 2: Overt modesty. Perseverance brings good fortune.

Fair prognosis. Vertigo with liver wind rising. Spastic pain in the legs and lower extremities. Venereal disease. Flushing-up of qi.

92

Line 3: Work of modesty. The superior person works things through. There is good fortune.

Fair prognosis. Digestive disorders. Venereal illnesses. Food poisoning. Spasms of the back muscles.

Line 4: There is nothing that does not improve with modest conduct.

Fair prognosis. Paralysis of the back and the legs. Joint pains. Mental exhaustion due to stress. Collapse of yin due to bleeding.

Line 5: No bragging of wealth before the neighbors. One should attack with force. There is nothing that will not improve.

Poor prognosis. May require surgery. Chest pains. Damp heat in the chest and the spleen. Paralysis of the legs.

Line 6: Overt modesty. One should send the armies to straighten up the country.

Fair prognosis. Venereal diseases. Persistent headaches. Flushing-up of the qi. Joint inflammation. Skin rashes. Paralysis of joints.

16. *Yu (Yü)*, Enthusiasm

Thunder comes rolling out of the earth,
The image of *Yu*.
The ancient kings played music to honor merits
And offered it with majesty to the Supreme Deity,
    glorifying their ancestors.

The Judgement: *Yu* means that one should obtain supporters and dispatch the army.

General Indications: Relatively long incubation before symptomatic manifestation. Rapid changes of symptomatology once the illness is apparent. Moving pains.

Specific Indications: Gastrointestinal disorders. Food stagnation. Sore throat. *Jing* essence insufficiency. Heart repletion symptoms. Trauma. Mental illness.

Moving lines

Line 1: One's enthusiasm is too obvious. There will be misfortune.

Fair prognosis. Paralysis of the legs. Diarrhea. Epilepsy. Muscle and joint pains.

Line 2: One is firm like a rock but not for a whole day. Perseverance brings good fortune.

Fair prognosis. Abdominal bleeding. Tumors in the lower abdomen.

Line 3: One's enthusiasm is like a dream. There will be remorse. Hesitation brings humiliation.

94

Poor prognosis. Abdominal abscesses. Peritonitis. Food poisoning with bleeding and vomiting. Exhaustion.

Line 4: One is like a fountain of enthusiasm. One achieves great goals. Do not doubt this. One's friends will gather all around them.

Fair prognosis. Great accumulation of toxins. Spleen and kidney vacuity. Diarrhea. Prostration from overexertion.

Line 5: One is chronically ill but still does not die.

Fair prognosis. At the end of a chronic illness. Tightness in the chest. Food stagnation. Vomiting. Illnesses from excessive sexual activities. Kidney yang vacuity. Impotence.

Line 6: One's enthusiasm is delusional but he is accomplished. If one changes, there will be no blame.

Fair prognosis. Wrong medicine may have been given. Change physician. Heat in the head and cold in the feet. Headaches with vertigo. Sexual excess.

17. *Sui (Sui)*, Following

Thunder in the marsh,
The image of *Sui*.
The superior person thus goes indoors
   for rest and regeneration.

The Judgement: *Sui* means great success. Perseverance brings good fortune. There is no fault in this.

General Indications: Damp diseases. Fluid and cold stagnation. Venereal diseases. Severe prostration. Diseases of multiple etiologies. Possible coma or death.

Specific Indications: Food stagnation. Toxic state due to blood stasis. Vomiting. Mental stagnation. Sexual problems.

Moving lines

Line 1: The public officials are changing their attitude. Perseverance brings good fortune. Mingling with outsiders brings success.

Good prognosis. Leg pains. Food stagnation. Diarrhea. Depression. Benefit from walking in the fresh air and sun.

Line 2: If one clings to the small child, they will lose the strong man.

Poor prognosis. Change physician. Danger of misdiagnosis. Danger of death. Food stagnation with vomiting. Cold extremities. Joint pains. Epilepsy of children.

Line 3: If one clings to the strong man, they will lose the small child. Through following, one finds what one seeks. Perseverance brings good fortune.

Fair prognosis by radical treatment. Sudden changes of symptomatology. Heart diseases. Constipation. Vomiting. Contagious febrile diseases.

Line 4: Success by following. Perseverance brings misfortune. Sincerity about one's path brings clarity. How can there be any fault in this?

Fair prognosis. May be beneficial to obtain a second opinion. Needs immediate treatment. Chest pain. Bleeding from the mouth. Mental depression.

Line 5: The goodness of the inner truth. There will be good fortune.

Poor prognosis with sudden change in symptoms. Possible death. Brain disorders. Mental illness. The liver overpowering the spleen. Oversensitivity of the nervous system. Hysteria. Flushing-up of the qi.

Line 6: One has joined the solid alliance and is still tied to it. The king offers them to the Western Mountains.

Poor prognosis. Possible death. Brain tumor. Anorexia. Aphasia.

18. *Gu (Ku)*, Work on What Has Been Spoiled (Decay)

The wind blows down on the mountain,
The image of *Gu*.
Thus the superior person inspires the people
   to improve their conduct.

The Judgement: *Gu* means supreme success. One should cross the great river. Before the beginning, three days. After the beginning, three days.

General Indications: Very chronic diseases caused by long-term stress, poor diet, sexual excess, and unhappiness. Requires radical treatment such as surgery. Possible death.

Specific Indications: Chronic wind diseases. Stubborn venereal diseases. Parasitic infestations. Esophageal cancer. Liver conquering the spleen. Mental derangement. Epilepsy of children.

Moving lines

Line 1: One should correct their father's mistake. If there is a son, the deceased father is free of blame. There may be danger. But there will be good fortune in the end.

Fair prognosis. Requires immediate attention. Congenital problems, especially from father's blood line. Pain and swelling of lower extremities. Headaches. Hemorrhoids. Sudden death of father.

Line 2: One should correct their mother's mistake. One should not stay too persevering.

Fair prognosis. Very slow and gradual progress. Inherited weakness, especially from mother's family. Trauma to legs.

98

Paralysis of extremities. Syphilis. Bone diseases. Sudden death of mother.

Line 3: One should correct their father's mistake. There will be a little remorse. But there will be no great blame.

Poor prognosis. Genetic problems, especially from father's line. Lower abdominal tumor. Venereal disease. Food poisoning. Medicine may be too old to work. Hemorrhoids due to toxins.

Line 4: One is escalating their father's mistake. To continue will bring humiliation.

Poor prognosis. Congenital illnesses which exacerbate quickly. Wind heat in the lungs. Damp heat in the stomach. Chronic problems triggered by fever. Gastrointestinal infections. Terminal syphilis.

Line 5: One is correcting his father's mistake. One should be praised.

Poor prognosis. Severe wind diseases. Virulent contagious diseases leading to paralysis or death. Stroke. Severe contagious dysentery. Extreme exhaustion.

Line 6: One is not in the imperial service. One sets up higher standards.

Poor prognosis. Right before death or complete failure of bodily functions. Collapse of yin and yang. Brain damage. Extreme emaciation.

19. *Lin (Lin)*, Approach

The earth above the marsh,
The image of *Lin*.
The superior person is thus tireless in their will
    to teach
And limitless in their acceptance and protection of people.

The Judgement: *Lin* means supreme success. Perseverance brings good fortune. When the eighth month arrives, there will be misfortune.

General Indications: Generally deficient constitution. Congenital diseases. Diseases caused by prenatal shock. Liver/spleen disharmony. Systemically toxic state. Lack of mental ability. Two concurrent pathologies.

Specific Indications: Blood stasis in the abdomen. Spleen vacuity. Indigestion. Constipation. Lung weakness. Menstrual problems.

Moving lines

Line 1: Mutual approach. Perseverance brings good fortune.

Fair prognosis. Edema of the feet. Severe diarrhea. Sudden discharge of toxins. Disorders of the nervous system. Gastrointestinal infections.

Line 2: Mutual approach. There will be good fortune. Nothing that will not improve.

Fair prognosis. Exacerbation right before recovery. Exhaustion of the *jing* essence. Pain of the legs from wind *bi* syndrome. Severe pain in lower limbs.

100

Line 3: Easy approach. Nothing improves. If one has already repented, they are free from blame.

Fair prognosis. Complete recovery to health in the case of a mild illness. Poor prognosis for chronic, severe problems. Blood stasis in the abdomen. Severe lower back pain. Constipation. Generalized edema. Toxic state.

Line 4: Thorough approach. There is no fault in this.

Fair prognosis. Oral irritation by wind heat. Diseases of sexual origin. Severe subcostal spasms. Abdominal infections. Uterine spasms.

Line 5: Wise approach. This is correct for a great prince. There will be good fortune.

Poor prognosis. Heat in the upper burner. Toxic conditions in the chest and abdomen. Joint pains. Vomiting.

Line 6: Generous approach. There will be good fortune. There is no fault in this.

Poor prognosis. Severe heat in the upper burner. Liver heat rising to the head. Brain dysfunctions. Epilepsy. Constipation. Utmost exhaustion.

20. *Guan (Kuan)*, Contemplation (View)

The wind blows over the earth,
The image of *Guan*.
The ancient kings thus reviewed all the regions
and gave them instructions.

The Judgement: *Guan* means that the hands have been already washed, but yet no offering has been made. With sincerity, they will worship one.

General Indications: Unstable mental state. Brain disorders. Confusion. Liver wind causing pain, spasms, and paralysis. Prostration.

Specific Indications: Headaches. Brain dysfunction. Neurasthenia. Vertigo. Flushing-up. Insomnia. Mental derangement. Shoulder spasms. Paralysis of lower back and legs. Vaginal bleeding.

Moving lines

Line 1: Immature view. It is no fault for an inferior person. But this is humiliation for a superior person.

Fair prognosis. Exacerbation of illness. Liver yang repletion. Wind paralysis of the legs. Epilepsy. Severe spastic pain of legs.

Line 2: Peeping through the crack of the door. It is good for a woman to be persevering.

Good prognosis. Very penetrating diagnosis. Wind damp in the legs. Flu. Food poisoning. Boils. Diarrhea. Toxic state of the lower burner. Mental confusion from sexual excess.

102

Line 3: I will reflect on my life and decide whether to proceed or to retreat.

Fair prognosis. Gradual exacerbation. Severe wind diseases. Severe back pain. Food stagnation. Stroke in the elderly.

Line 4: The glorious view of the kingdom. It is good to be invited by the king.

Fair prognosis. Stagnant toxins in the middle burner. Stomach pain. Severe flu. Stomach qi vacuity leading to anorexia.

Line 5: I reflect on my life. The superior person is without blame.

Poor outlook. Possible death. Collapse of yin and yang. Paralysis. Severe depression.

Line 6: One reflects on their life. The superior person is without blame.

Poor prognosis. Possible death. Severe brain diseases. Toxic boils on the head. Severe eye infections leading to blindness.

21. *Shi He (Shih Ho)*, Biting Through

Thunder and lightning,
The image of *Shi He*.
The ancient kings thus made firm laws
  and clearly defined the penalties.

The Judgement: *Shi He* means success. It is good to deliver justice.

General Indications: Chronic illnesses that are hard to eliminate. Liver fire rising to the heart. Heart fire repletion. Blockage in circulation, food passage, or airways. Fever which moves very rapidly. Stubborn symptoms.

Specific Indications: Epigastric blockage. Food stagnation. Constipation. Spasms of extremities. Abdominal abscess. Toothache. Sore throat. Diseases of the mouth. Hoarseness.

Moving lines

Line 1: One is put in the stocks. One's feet cannot be seen.

Fair prognosis. Blood stasis in the legs. Painful illnesses of the extremities. Food poisoning. Fever.

Line 2: One bites into the tender flesh. One's nose cannot be seen.

Good prognosis if treated gently by a good physician. Phlegm in the lung. Heart heat rising to the mouth. Coughs. Toxic conditions in the stomach. Toothache. Diseases of the nose.

Line 3: One bites on old meat and is poisoned.

Fair prognosis. Extreme heat conditions. Severe eye diseases. Heart fire repletion. Food poisoning with fever and vomiting. Constipation. Dark red urine. Uterine bleeding.

Line 4: One bites on old, gristly meat and obtains golden arrows.

Fair prognosis. Radical treatment necessary. Digestive disorders. Gastrointestinal tumors. Internal bleeding.

Line 5: One bites on dried meat and obtains gold. Beware of danger. There will be good fortune.

Poor prognosis. Vacuity of the lungs and the heart. Heart diseases. Gastrointestinal problems. Edema. Blindness.

Line 6: One carries the cangue[10] around the neck. One's ears cannot be seen. There will be misfortune.

Poor prognosis. Liver yang rising to the head. Neck and shoulder pain. Epilepsy. Stroke. Deafness. Blindness.

---

[10]   A wooden collar 3-4 feet square used as a form of punishment in China to confine the head and sometimes hands

22. *Bi (Pi)*, Grace

Fire at the foot of a mountain,
The image of *Bi*.
Thus the superior person puts affairs in order
    and does not impose penalties.

The Judgement: *Bi* means success in small matters. It is good to take action.

General Indications: Chronic heart or spleen diseases. Superficial symptoms which do not necessarily reflect internal etiology. Internal heat. Damp heat in the lower burner. Death.

Specific Indications: Coronary heart disease. Spleen vacuity leading to indigestion, constipation. Boils from toxic conditions. Deterioration of vision. Infantile convulsions. Postpartum problems.

Moving lines

Line 1: One decorates their toes. Then they leave the carriage and walk.

Poor prognosis. Accumulation of heat causing cancer. Paralysis of the legs. Difficulty in walking. Indigestion. Spasms of neck and shoulder.

Line 2: One trims their beard.

Fair prognosis if treated radically. Damp heat in the legs. Constipation. Anuria. Edema. Leg pain. Sore throat. Severe headaches.

Line 3: One is very graceful and lustrous. Continuous perseverance brings good fortune.

Fair prognosis. Damp heat in the lower burner. Digestive problems. Heart diseases. Lower back pain.

Line 4: One is graceful and pure like the flying horse. One is a thief. They will woo a woman at the right time.

Fair prognosis. Damp heat in the stomach. Fever. Mental confusion. Convulsions. Contagious illnesses.

Line 5: One decorates the hills and the gardens. The silk roll is skimpy and small. There will be humiliation, but good fortune will come in the end.

Poor prognosis. Wind heat in the lungs. Bronchitis. Pneumonia with fever and chills. Heart pain. Possible death.

Line 6: Innocent refinement. There is no fault in this.

Poor prognosis. Wind paralysis. Stroke. Inoperable brain tumors. Vomiting of blood.

23. *Po (Po)*, Splitting Apart

The mountain on the earth,
The image of *Po*.
Thus those above give generously
    to those below to secure their positions.

The Judgement: *Po* means nothing should be undertaken.

General Indications: General degeneration. Deficiency weakness of the qi and blood. Yin and yang exhaustion. Chronic degenerative diseases leading to death.

Specific Indications: Weakening of all *zang* organs and *fu* bowels. Poor digestion and assimilation of food. Mental degeneration. Brain syphilis. Toxic condition of the entire body. Constant bleeding. Paralysis of shoulder and neck.

Moving lines

Line 1: The leg of the bed is broken. Those who stay firm will be ruined. There will be misfortune.

Fair prognosis. At the beginning of degeneration of yin and yang. Needs vigorous treatment to prevent further deterioration. Paralysis of the legs. Liver wind spasming the body with pain. Diarrhea with undigested food due to the spleen vacuity. Infection of the foot caused by trauma.

Line 2: The bed is broken on the edge. Those who stay firm will be ruined. There will be misfortune.

Fair prognosis. Danger of misdiagnosis. Kidney *jing* vacuity. Degeneration of the bones. Retention of urine. Vertigo. Food stagnation. Nausea. Tinnitus. Discharge of blood and pus.

Line 3: It is broken. There is no fault in this.

Poor prognosis. Very slow progress without surgery. Serious injury of the abdomen. Toxic condition causing boils. Food stagnation. Persistent pain in shoulder, neck, and extremities.

Line 4: The bed is broken up to the skin. There will be misfortune.

Poor prognosis. Degeneration furthers. Venereal disease. Painful subcostal spasms. Yin vacuity heat. Acute stomach disorder.

Line 5: Speared fish. Support will come from the courtesans. There is nothing that will not improve.

Poor prognosis. Perforation of the eardrum. Draining of boils. Gunshot wounds. Requires surgery or injections. Flu. Vertigo. Wind spasms of abdominal muscles. Stroke.

Line 6: One cannot eat the large fruit. The superior person receives a carriage. The inferior person loses their residence.

Poor diagnosis. Extreme exhaustion of yin and yang. Terminal illnesses. Terminal cancer. Vomiting and bleeding leading to death. Shock. Suicide.

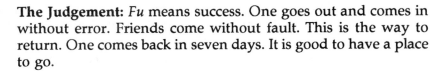

24. *Fu (Fu)*, Return (The Turning Point)

Thunder under the earth,
The image of *Fu*.
Thus the kings of antiquity closed the roads
    at the time of solstice.
Merchants and travellers then did not wander
    through the provinces.

The Judgement: *Fu* means success. One goes out and comes in without error. Friends come without fault. This is the way to return. One comes back in seven days. It is good to have a place to go.

General Indications: Sign of recovery from an illness. A turning point of an illness. Recurrence of illness. An illness may exacerbate temporarily but will eventually get well.

Specific Indications: Swelling of the foot. Subcostal spasms due to the liver wind. Sudden pains. Epilepsy. Pregnancy.

Moving lines

Line 1: One returns from a short distance. One has no remorse. There will be great good fortune.

Good prognosis. Recovery from a short-term illness. Liver wind rising. Foot pain. Sudden diarrhea.

Line 2: One returns safely. There will be good fortune.

Good prognosis. Gradual recovery. Interior heat with exterior chills. Abdominal pain. Stubborn cough. Edema.

110

Line 3: One returns frequently. There may be danger, but there is no blame in it.

Fair prognosis. The illness may recur frequently. May exacerbate if not treated properly. Lower back pain. Abdominal distention with pain. Weakening of vision. External cold and internal heat.

Line 4: One walks with others but returns alone.

Good prognosis. The illness may recur. Subcostal spasm due to the liver wind. Stomach disorders. Vomiting. Ascites.

Line 5: One returns majestically. There is no remorse.

Poor prognosis. Serious recurrence of an illness. Potent liver wind causing spasms and pains. Subcostal spasm. Night sweats. Depression from mental exertion.

Line 6: One is lost in returning. There will be misfortune. Everywhere there will be calamities. If the army is dispatched, there will be a huge loss in the end to the sovereign of the country. For ten years, one will not be able to strike again.

Good prognosis. Over the worst part of illness. Liver wind rising to the head. Headaches. Lack of appetite.

25. *Wu Wang (Wu Wang)*, Innocence (The Unexpected)

Thunder rolls under heaven,
The image of *Wu Wang*.
Everything has inborn innocence.
The ancient kings thus nourished all things
   in a timely manner.

The Judgement: *Wu Wang* means great success. Perseverance brings good progress. If one is not what they should be, there will be misfortune. One should not undertake anything.

General Indications: Sudden onset with severe symptoms but usually improves rapidly later. Problems caused by liver wind. Mental anguish. Strong side-effects of drugs.

Specific Indications: Headaches. Subcostal spasms. Epigastric pain. Edema. Lack of appetite. Depression.

Moving lines

Line 1: Innocent behavior brings good fortune.

Fair prognosis if natural substances and therapy are used. Severe pain in the foot. Heart diseases. Mental depression. Severe diarrhea.

Line 2: One does not cultivate for harvest. One does not plow for reward. Therefore, it is good to have a place to go.

Good prognosis even though symptoms may be severe at the onset. Leg pain. Severe coughing. Vomiting. Flushing-up. Edema. Mental stress.

112

Line 3: One meets with misfortune that they do not deserve. The cow that was fastened by someone can be the traveller's gain and the townsman's loss.

Fair prognosis. Sudden loss of health in spite of maintenance of good habits. Sudden accident. Seasonal contagious diseases. Abdominal pains. Poor vision. High fever. Constipation.

Line 4: One should persevere. Then they are without blame.

Fair prognosis. Slow recovery. Spastic flank pain. Flu. Boils.

Line 5: One did not become sick by one's own fault. Do not take any medicine. The disease will pass of itself.

Good prognosis. Danger of misdiagnosis. Do not prescribe medicine. Contagious diseases of the chest. Indigestion. Latent fever. Subcostal spasm and pain. Mental confusion.

Line 6: Naive action brings misfortune. Nothing improves.

Poor prognosis. Liver wind rising to the head. Stubborn cough. Severe headaches. Oropharyngeal pain. Breathing difficulty. Vomiting.

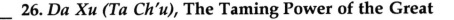

26. *Da Xu (Ta Ch'u)*, The Taming Power of the Great

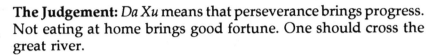

Heaven in the mountain,
The image of *Da Xu*.
The superior person thus studies the wisdom
   and behavior of ancient sages
To cultivate their character.

The Judgement: *Da Xu* means that perseverance brings progress. Not eating at home brings good fortune. One should cross the great river.

General Indications: Serious accumulations of toxins. Illnesses due to chronic stress. Symptoms worse at night than during the daytime. Overbearing symptoms.

Specific Indications: Severe headaches. Chronic cough. Tuberculosis. Depression. Spasms of the whole body. Constipation with abdominal pain. Anuria. Boils.

Moving lines

Line 1: One has a dagger in their hand but they must restrain themself.

Fair prognosis. Degenerative wind diseases. Leg pain with spasms. Splitting headaches. Persistent diarrhea. Breathing difficulty. Boils. Children's temper tantrums due to liver yang repletion.

Line 2: The wagon wheels have no spokes.

Poor prognosis. Heat rising to the upper burner. High fever with constipation and anuria. Severe headaches with abdominal pain. Vomiting of blood. Rectal bleeding. Hemorrhoids. Pneumonia.

Line 3: Good horses run after others. Beware of danger and stay firm. One practices riding and martial arts. It is good to have a place to go.

Fair prognosis. Slow recovery. Stagnation of toxins in the abdomen. Joint pain. Lower back pain. Diseases of mouth and throat.

Line 4: The headboard for a young bull. There will be great good fortune.

Fair prognosis. Great heat in the chest. Severe subcostal spasms. High fever. Constipation. Stupor.

Line 5: The tusks of a spayed boar. There will be good fortune.

Fair prognosis. Slow recovery. Wind injury of the chest. Excessive mental stress. Abdominal distention. Flu with dislike of heat.

Line 6: One masters the path of heaven. There will be success.

Good prognosis. Return to health. Slight possibility of exacerbation. Severe headaches.

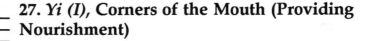

27. *Yi (I)*, Corners of the Mouth (Providing Nourishment)

Thunder under the mountain,
The image of *Yi*.
The superior person is thus careful of their words
    and moderate in eating and drinking.

The Judgement: *Yi* means that perseverance brings good fortune. Pay attention to nourishment and to what you want to put into your mouth.

General Indications: Diseases from deep internal causes. Diseases of the spleen and stomach. Diseases of the tongue. Slow recovery. Problems with diet and nutrition. Possible death.

Specific Indications: Food stagnation. Internal abscess. Heart heat appearing in the mouth. Deep toxins. Diseases of oral cavity. Malnutrition.

Moving lines

Line 1: One lets go of their magic turtle and looks at others with their mouths bulging. There will be misfortune.

Poor prognosis. Disharmony of qi and blood. Indigestion. Paralysis of extremities. Emaciation from fever. Sudden death.

Line 2: One turns to their inferiors for nourishment. This is not proper conduct. One then turns to the hill for nourishment. To go on like this will bring misfortune.

Fair prognosis. Danger of wrong treatment. Extremely malnourished conditions. Leg pains. Joint problem. Cough. Gum problems.

116

Line 3: One turns away from nourishment. Perseverance brings misfortune. Do not act thus for ten years. Nothing will improve.

Fair prognosis. Requires treatment for a long time. Chronic infections of the genitalia. Headaches. Fever. Constipation.

Line 4: One turns to their superiors for nourishment. Good fortune. One snoops around with piercing eyes like a tiger with insatiable craving. There is no blame in this.

Poor prognosis. Damp heat in the abdomen. Heart heat appearing in the mouth. Severe chest pains. Fever and chills. Oral infections. Constipation. Early stage of cancer.

Line 5: One deviates from the right path. Perseverance brings good fortune. One should not cross the great river.

Fair prognosis. Slow recovery. Wind cold in the chest. A febrile contagious diseases. Tightness in the chest. Pneumonia.

Line 6: The source of nourishment. Beware of danger. There will be good fortune. One should cross the great river.

Fair prognosis. Severe headaches. Severe damp heat in the upper burner. Malnutrition. Emaciation.

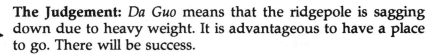

28. *Da Guo (Ta Kuo)*, Preponderance of the Great

The marsh covers the trees,
The image of *Da Guo*.
Thus the superior person is independent without fear.
They are without concern
  even if they have to renounce the world.

The Judgement: *Da Guo* means that the ridgepole is sagging down due to heavy weight. It is advantageous to have a place to go. There will be success.

General Indications: Overwhelming pathogenic forces weakening the qi and blood. Conditions of yang repletion and yin vacuity. Overstressed and overexhausted condition. Usually poor prognosis. Possible death.

Specific Indications: Persistent vomiting. Abdominal mass. Food stagnation. Edema. Stroke. Epilepsy. Mental overexhaustion. Problems due to excessive eating or drinking. Blood stasis in lower abdomen.

Moving lines

Line 1: One spreads white cogan grass underneath. There is no blame in this.

Fair prognosis. Wind paralysis of the foot. Edema of the legs. Dyspnea. Constipation. Vomiting.

Line 2: An old poplar sprouts at the root. An old man takes a young woman for wife. There is nothing that will not improve.

Poor prognosis in spite of temporary improvement. Return of yang. Spleen vacuity. Kidney yang vacuity. Venereal diseases.

118

Sexual dysfunction. Leg pain. Paralysis of lower back. Intermittent vomiting. Subcostal spasm.

Line 3: The ridgepole is sagging down due to heavy weight. There will be misfortune.

Fair prognosis. Slow recovery. *Jing* essence vacuity. Cold in the lower back. Diarrhea. Rectal bleeding.

Line 4: The ridgepole is well supported. There will be good fortune. Ulterior motives bring humiliation.

Fair prognosis. Cold dampness in the middle burner. Severe diarrhea. Heart qi vacuity. Poisoning. Ear problem. Diseases of the mouth.

Line 5: The old poplar flowers. The old woman takes a man for husband. No blame. No praise.

Fair prognosis. Sudden recovery. Return of yin. Sexual problems. Chest pain. Stomach ulcer with pain. Stubborn cough with breathing difficulty.

Line 6: One arrogantly tries to swim across the river and gets their neck under the water. There will be misfortune but there is no blame in it.

Poor prognosis. Extreme kidney yang vacuity due to sexual excess. Water stagnation. Severe headaches. Stroke with aphasia.

29. *Kan (K'an)*, The Abysmal (Water)

Water flows profusely and reaches its goal,
The image of *Kan*.
The superior person thus practices virtue
   and continues their teaching.

The Judgement: *Kan* means danger. Be sincere. Then there will be success at heart. Whatever one does will bring success.

General Indications: Generally dangerous situation. Serious conditions. Diseases from remote origins. Cold and damp illnesses. Very toxic conditions. Blood diseases.

Specific Indications: Vacuity of the liver, kidneys, and spleen. Diarrhea. Water retention. Night sweats. Bleeding. Venereal diseases. Ear problem. Excessive menstruation. Nervous breakdown.

Moving lines

Line 1: One falls to the bottom of the pit. There will be misfortune.

Poor prognosis. Water and phlegm stagnation. Cold extremities. Anorexia. Food poisoning. Joint pains.

Line 2: The abyss is perilous. Yet there will be small gains.

Poor prognosis. Severe kidney and spleen vacuity. Bleeding. Pus. Paralysis of the limbs. Diarrhea. Postpartum depression.

Line 3: One comes and goes, passing abyss over abyss. One stops and looks at the danger or they will fall into the pit. Do not act.

Poor prognosis. Damp cold in the abdomen. Vomiting. Severe diarrhea. Abscess on the lower back.

Line 4: A barrel of wine and a dish of rice. The clay mug is modestly served through the window. There is no blame in the end.

Poor prognosis. Liver wind causing pains. Kidney *jing* vacuity. Severe subcostal spasm. Alcohol poisoning. Inability to eat. Vomiting. Abdominal pain.

Line 5: The abyss is not full to the point of overflowing. It is only filled to the brim. There is no blame in this.

Poor prognosis. Severe chills. Convulsions. Paralysis of the extremities. Illness due to abortion.

Line 6: One is tied up with cords and ropes and locked up in between thorn-hedged walls. For three years one cannot get out.

Poor prognosis. Phlegm misting the portals of the heart. Mental derangement. Hysteria. Headaches. Blindness. Bad cold. Anorexia.

30. *Li (Li)*, The Clinging (Fire)

Brightness rises twice,
The image of *Li*.
Thus the great person illumines the four corners
   of the world
By maintaining their brilliance.

The Judgement: *Li* means that one should persevere. There will be success. Taking care of a cow will bring good fortune.

General Indications: Illness caused by heat. Fever. Aggressive illnesses. Heart diseases. Emotional cause of illness. Inflammation. Usually poor prognosis.

Specific Indications: Cardiovascular diseases. Subcostal spasm. Heat in the lower burner. Mass in the abdomen. Breast infection. Headaches due to heat. Emotional outbursts. Eye infections. Hoarseness.

Moving lines

Line 1: The footprints are crisscross. Be respectful. There is no blame in this.

Fair prognosis. *Tai yang* stage. Early febrile disease. Hot swelling of the legs. Paralysis of the limbs. Mental confusion.

Line 2: Yellow brilliance. There will be supreme good fortune.

Fair prognosis with sudden change of symptomatology. *Yang ming* stage of aggressive, contagious diseases. Acute gastroenteritis. Heat stroke. Constipation. Abdominal mass. Edema in the legs.

Line 3: The brightness of the setting sun. One cannot beat the pot and sing. Thus one mourns over their old age. There will be misfortune.

Poor prognosis. Madness due to the liver yang repletion. Vacuity of the qi and blood. Persistent vomiting. Severe mental anguish.

Line 4: It comes suddenly, it flames up, it dies out, and it is thrown away.

Very poor prognosis. Severe spleen vacuity. Cardiac arrest. Paraplegia. Possible death.

Line 5: Tears flow in floods. People sigh and mourn, but there will be good fortune.

Poor prognosis. Cardiac failure. Dyspnea. Vertigo. Contagious febrile diseases. Eye infections.

Line 6: The king dispatches the army. There is exhilaration. He dismisses the leader. It is not a shame to take captives. There is no blame in this.

Poor prognosis. Heart attack. Extremely grave condition. Death from severe febrile disease. Head injury.

31. *Xian (Hsien)*, Influence (Wooing)

The marsh on the mountain,
The image of *Xian*.
The superior person thus humbles themself
and accepts people.

The Judgement: *Xian* means success. One should persevere. Taking a woman for wife brings good fortune.

General Indications: Infectious diseases. External causes of illness. Affliction from venereal origin. Sexual excess. Interior heat and exterior cold. Congenital illnesses.

Specific Indications: Contagious illnesses. Venereal diseases. Lower abdominal pain. Heavy limbs. Headaches. Food stagnation. Liver cancer.

Moving lines

Line 1: One senses their big toes.

Fair prognosis if treated at onset, or gradual exacerbation. Contagious disease. Latent fever. Problem of oral cavity. Constipation due to heat. Hysteria. Nosebleed.

Line 2: One senses their calves. There will be misfortune. Procrastination brings good fortune.

Fair prognosis. Painful spasm of legs. Depression due to mental stress. Flu.

Line 3: One senses their thighs. Hold on to whatever follows. To go on brings humiliation.

124

Fair prognosis. Vigorous therapy needed for recovery. Food stagnation. Damp heat in the middle burner. Severe diarrhea. Venereal disease. Jaundice. Lower back pain. Neurosis of children.

Line 4: Perseverance brings good fortune. Remorse disappears. One is disturbed and their mind wanders yet one's friends follow one's ideas.

Fair prognosis. Kidney vacuity. Anxiety. Nervous breakdown. Sexual excess. Lower back pain. Genital problems.

Line 5: One senses the back of their neck. There will be no remorse.

Poor prognosis. Epilepsy. Apoplexy. Asthma. Gastrointestinal cancer. Death.

Line 6: One senses their jaws, cheeks, and tongue.

Poor prognosis. Brain disorders. Meningitis. General edema. Tuberculosis.

32. *Heng (Hêng)*, Duration

Thunder and wind,
The image of *Heng*.
The superior person thus firmly adheres
  to their enduring principles.

The Judgement: *Heng* means success without blame. One should persevere. Nothing should be undertaken.

General Indications: Constant state of illness. Pains from wind. Chronic diseases from long-term stress, poor diet, and toxic life style. Extremely slow recovery.

Specific Indications: Chronic stomach stress due to poor dietary habits. Vomiting. Abdominal pain. Edema of lower extremities. Nervous breakdown due to chronic stress.

Moving lines

Line 1: Hasty undertaking. Perseverance brings misfortune. Nothing will improve.

Fair prognosis. Paralysis of the foot due to wind. Abdominal pain. Meningitis of children. Exacerbation of cold. Qi flushing up to the heart. Diseases of sexual etiology.

Line 2: Remorse disappears.

Fair prognosis. Chronic qi and blood vacuity. Pain in the legs. Abdominal spasm and pain due to wind. Diarrhea due to cold in the spleen.

Line 3: One's virtue is not consistent. One will be embarrassed. There will be constant humiliation.

126

Fair prognosis. Slow recovery. Damp cold in the lower burner. Diarrhea. Abdominal tumor. Bleeding. Venereal disease. Diseases of the throat.

Line 4: There is no game in the field.

Fair prognosis. Try new medicine and change diet. Spleen/stomach disharmony. Abdominal pain due to toxins.

Line 5: One's virtue should be consistent. Good fortune for a woman but misfortune for a man.

Fair prognosis. Female problems will get better. Exacerbation of chronic illnesses. Diarrhea and vomiting. Spasms of the chest and back. Dyspnea. Abdominal mass. Diseases of oral cavity.

Line 6: Fluctuation in endurance will bring misfortune.

Poor prognosis. Severe liver disease. Collapse of yin and yang. Cardiac arrest. Extreme mental stress. Blindness. Vertigo.

33. *Dun (Tun)*, Retreat

Mountain under heaven,
The image of *Dun*.
Thus the superior person keeps
   the inferior person away
Without anger but with reserve.

The Judgement: *Dun* means success. Perseverance brings good fortune in small things.

General Indications: Acute illnesses tend to improve very quickly, but chronic diseases may have grave consequences. Sudden loss of qi and *shen* spirit. Liver qi stagnation. Epigastric spasm from heart qi vacuity. Kidney vacuity manifestations in the lower abdomen.

Specific Indications: Sudden exhaustion. Severe diarrhea. Fluid stagnation in the upper burner. Edema. Sudden death. Suicide.

Moving lines

Line 1: Retreating at the tail. There may be danger. One should not undertake anything.

Fair prognosis. Vacuity heat in the heart or spleen. Lung heat. Trauma to the foot.

Line 2: Someone holds them tight with yellow oxhide. They cannot be torn loose.

Fair prognosis. Wind in the middle burner. Stroke. Paralysis. Venereal diseases. Traumatic arthritis.

Line 3: Arrested retreat. Sickness and danger. It brings good fortune to retain servants and maids.

Fair prognosis. Spleen/stomach disharmony. Painful stagnation of qi in the stomach. General stagnation of qi. Paralysis of the entire body. Edema from fluid stagnation. Depression. Diseases from dampness. Morning sickness from damp heat in the stomach.

Line 4: Intentional retreat. It brings good fortune to the superior person and destruction to the inferior person.

Fair prognosis. Spleen vacuity. Food stagnation in the middle burner. Abdominal pain. Painful limbs. Wind disease in the interior.

Line 5: Amicable retreat. Perseverance brings good fortune.

Poor prognosis. Collapsed *shen*. Severe qi and fluid stagnation. Nervous breakdown. Chest pains. Alternating chills and fever. Weakening of eyesight.

Line 6: Joyful retreat. Everything improves.

Fair prognosis. Severe qi stagnation. Depression. Headaches. Phlegm stagnation in the upper burner. Sexual exhaustion.

34. *Da Zhuang (Ta Chuang)*, The Power of the Great

Thunder above heaven,
The image of *Da Zhuang*.
The superior person thus does not follow a path
  that does not conform the proper order.

The Judgement: *Da Zhuang* means that perseverance brings good fortune.

General Indication: Extremely aggressive illnesses. Powerful febrile diseases. Liver repletion.

Specific Indications: Severe headaches. Spasms of muscles. Fluid stagnation of the lower burner. Liver wind rising to the heart. Qi flushing up to the head. Constipation. Qi and food stagnation in the middle burner. Diseases caused by excessive eating and drinking. Diseases of the nails. Measles.

Moving lines

Line 1: Strength in the toes. To keep going brings misfortune. This is the truth.

Fair prognosis. Afflictions due to excessive eating. Serious qi stagnation in the lower extremities. Severe spasms of the foot. Contagious illness. Stomach qi rebelling up to the head. Hysteric attacks.

Line 2: Perseverance brings good fortune.

Fair prognosis. Heat in the lungs and heart. Infectious febrile diseases. Severe stomach cramps due to damp heat in the stomach. Constipation.

130

Line 3: The inferior person uses power. The superior person does not use power. To continue is dangerous. The goat butts against the hedge and his horns become entangled.

Fair prognosis. Phlegm stagnation in the lungs causing coughs. Lung qi vacuity. Pain in the lower back due to cold. Heart vacuity due to heat. Boils on the extremities.

Line 4: Perseverance brings good fortune. Remorse disappears. The hedge is open and there is no entanglement. Power lies in the axle of a great cart.

Fair prognosis. Abdominal pains due to qi stagnation. Liver qi rising to cause epilepsy.

Line 5: One loosens the goat with ease. There is no remorse.

Poor prognosis. Collapsed *shen*. Severe lung qi vacuity. Stupor. Vomiting. Exhaustion. Spermatorrhea. Constipation. Anuria. Eye pains. Cold stagnation in the extremities.

Line 6: The goat butts against the hedge. It cannot go backward. It cannot go forward. Nothing improves. But this difficulty will bring good fortune.

Fair prognosis. Liver wind rising to the head. Headaches. Vertigo. High fevers. Extreme weakening of vision.

35. *Jin (Chin)*, Progress

Brightness appears over the earth,
The image of *Jin*.
The superior person thus brightens their
    brilliant character.

The Judgement: *Jin* means that the great lord is honored with many horses. In a single day, one is entertained three times.

General Indications: Progressive diseases. Gradual exacerbation leading to fatal consequences. Active course of an illness.

Specific Indications: Heart diseases. Contagious illnesses. Heat stroke. Toxic state. Splitting headaches. Upper burner hot and lower burner cold. Boils on the foot. Dry throat. Mental derangement. Loss of olfactory sensations.

Moving lines

Line 1: One progresses but is blocked. Perseverance brings good fortune. If one is not confident, they should keep quiet. There is no blame in this.

Fair prognosis. Flushing-up of qi causing palpitations and mental confusion. Stomachache due to damp heat. Spleen vacuity leading to diarrhea. Swelling of the foot.

Line 2: One progresses but is despondent. Perseverance brings good fortune. One will be blessed by their ancestress.

Fair prognosis. Kidney *jing* vacuity. Sexual exhaustion. Cold damp spleen leading to diarrhea. Qi and blood stagnation in the abdomen. Knee pain from infection.

Line 3: One is gratified all over. Remorse disappears.

Fair prognosis. Spasms of abdominal muscles due to cold stagnation. Night sweats from yin vacuity. Exhaustion of the blood. Weakening of vision and hearing. Kidney *jing* vacuity.

Line 4: One progresses like a hamster. Perseverance brings danger.

Fair prognosis. Stomach qi vacuity. Epigastric pains due to stagnation of qi and food. Food poisoning. Alternating chills and fever.

Line 5: Remorse disappears. Do not take loss and gain to heart. To go on brings good fortune. Everything improves.

Poor prognosis. Occasional miraculous recovery. Chronic lung vacuity. Qi stagnation of the chest and abdomen causing pains. Poor vision. Headaches. Edema due to fluid stagnation. Great fever from exterior cold invasion.

Line 6: Progress with the horns. It only vanquishes the village. Awareness of danger brings good fortune. There is no blame in this. Perseverance brings misfortune.

Fair prognosis. Subcostal spasm and headaches due to the liver wind. High fever. Vomiting from food poisoning. Meningitis in children.

36. *Ming Yi (Ming I)*, Darkening of the Light

The sun sets under the earth,
The image of *Ming Yi*.
Thus the superior person lives with the masses.
They cover their brightness yet it still glows.

The Judgement: *Ming Yi* means that one should persevere in times of adversity.

General Indications: Hidden cause of illness needs further investigation. Diseases of unknown etiology. Often misdiagnosed. Problems of the middle burner. Loss of mental clarity. Death.

Specific Indications: Spleen/stomach disharmony. Cancers of the digestive system. Interior heat stagnation. Constipation. Eye problem. Exhaustion.

Moving lines

Line 1: Darkening of the light during flight. One lowers one's wings. When the superior person travels, they do not eat for three days. They have a place to go. The host will gossip about them.

Fair prognosis. Spleen vacuity. Qi and blood stagnation in the middle burner. Kidney vacuity leading to restless *shen*. Mental exhaustion. Paralysis of the limbs. Wind stroke in the elderly. Cold stagnation in the lower extremities.

Line 2: Darkening of the light injures one in their left thigh. Helping with a powerful horse brings great fortune.

Fair prognosis. Damp heat in the stomach. Headaches. Vertigo.

134

Foot pains. Edema from fluid stagnation.

Line 3: Darkening of the light during the chase in the south. One captures the great leader. One should not be swift to persevere.

Fair prognosis. Painful spasms of lower back and legs due to qi stagnation. Qi flushing up to the head causing dizziness. Eye diseases. Fits of children due to the liver qi rebelling up to the head.

Line 4: One pierces the left side of their abdomen to get at the heart of the dark light. One goes out from the gate of the courtyard.

Poor prognosis. May require surgery. Severe abdominal pain from qi stagnation. Painful constipation in descending colon.

Line 5: Prince Ji covered his light. Perseverance brings good fortune.

Poor prognosis. Collapsed *shen*. Severe *jing* vacuity. Alternating chills and fever. Nervous breakdown. Severe chest pains. Ear diseases.

Line 6: There is no brightness, but darkness. First, one climbs up to heaven. Then one plunges into the earth.

Fair prognosis. Anorexia due to stomach qi vacuity. Headaches caused by liver wind. Boils on the face. Ear infections.

37. *Jia Ren (Chia Jên)*, The Family (Clan)

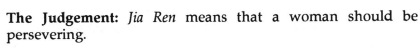

Wind comes out of fire,
The image of *Jia Ren*.
The superior person thus says what they mean
   and operates with consistency.

The Judgement: *Jia Ren* means that a woman should be persevering.

General Indications: Contagious diseases. Illnesses inherited in the family. Genetic disorders. Maladies originating from overindulgence. Heart diseases caused by emotional stress. Stagnation of the seven emotions.

Specific Indications: Congenital diseases. Spleen vacuity leading to general weakness. Flu. Constipation with gas. Kidney yang vacuity. Sexual weakness due to indulgence. Alternating chills and fever. Edema. Boils from toxic stagnant conditions. Menstrual irregularities.

Moving lines

Line 1: Hiding in the house. Remorse disappears.

Good prognosis. Beginning of wind invasion. Paralysis of the lower extremities. Heat stagnation in the stomach causing depression.

Line 2: She should not daydream. She must work in the kitchen. Perseverance brings good fortune.

Fair prognosis. Depression due to qi stagnation. Edema of the legs. Contagious febrile diseases. Wind eye. Blood stasis in a woman.

Line 3: When the family members talk loudly, there will be remorse. Good fortune comes nevertheless. When women and children giggle loudly, there is humiliation.

Fair prognosis with slow recovery. Qi vacuity in the lungs. Liver yang repletion. Fluid stagnation in the abdomen. Ascites. Ear infections. Irregular menstruation. Miscarriage.

Line 4: A wealthy family. Great good fortune.

Fair prognosis. Chronic lung problems with persistent cough. Summer heat stroke. Food and fluid stagnation in the middle burner.

Line 5: One attends one's family like a king. Do not fear anything. There will be good fortune.

Fair prognosis. May benefit from changing medication. Liver qi rebelling up to the head. Alternating chills and fever. Headaches. Hysteria. Collapsed *shen*. Nervous breakdown. Hemiplegia due to stroke.

Line 6: One's authority commands respect. In the end, there is good fortune.

Fair prognosis. Chills and fever. Headaches. Weakening of vision or hearing.

38. *Kui (K'uei)*, Opposition

Fire above, the marsh below,
The image of *Kui*.
The superior person thus maintains their
   individuality
When socializing with others.

The Judgement: *Kui* means good fortune in small matters.

General Indications: Sudden onset and rapid progress of disease but fair prognosis for recovery in the end. Contradictory symptoms. May involve gross negligence in medical practice such as wrong diagnosis or prescription.

Specific Indications: Kidney *jing* vacuity. Lung diseases. Contagious illnesses. Toxic state from food stagnation. Mental confusion. Liver qi rebelling up to the head. Hysteria. Exterior heat and interior cold. Hemiplegia. Boils. Blood stasis after abortion.

Moving lines

Line 1: Remorse disappears. Even if one loses their horse, one does not need to run after it. It will return on its own. When one sees an evil person, protect oneself against mistakes.

Fair prognosis. Beginning of flu. Alternating chills and fever. Leg pain due to cold stagnation. Diarrhea.

Line 2: One runs into their master in the alley. There is no blame in this.

Fair prognosis. Liver diseases with subcostal spasms. Lung diseases. Leg pains. Food stagnation. Food poisoning.

Line 3: One sees a wagon pulled back. The cow is stopped. The driver's hair and nose are cut off. This is not a good beginning. But it is a good end.

Fair prognosis. Fluid and food stagnation in the abdomen. Constipation. Edema. Spleen vacuity. Emaciation with weak limbs. Dyspnea. Arrhythmia.

Line 4: One is isolated by opposition but meets a great man with whom one can affiliate. Despite the danger, there is no blame in this.

Fair prognosis. Food poisoning with severe abdominal pain. Prostration.

Line 5: Remorse disappears. One's master bites through the flesh. How can it be a mistake to go along with him?

Fair prognosis. Heat and qi flushing up in the upper burner. Cold stagnation in the lower burner. Phlegm stagnation. Facial edema. Weakening of vision. Fungal infection. Syphilis.

Line 6: One is isolated by opposition. One sees a pig covered with dirt. One sees a cart full of devils. First one draws a bow on them. Then one lays the bow down. One is not a robber. One will marry at the right time. The rain will come as you go. Then, you will have good fortune.

Poor prognosis. Unconsciousness. Mental derangement. Severe headaches with vertigo. High fever. Abdominal pain.

39. *Jian (Chien)*, Obstruction

Water on the mountain,
The image of *Jian*.
The superior person thus reflects on themself
    and cultivates their character.

The Judgement: *Jian* means that one should go southwest. One should not go northeast. One should see the great person. Perseverance brings good fortune.

General Indications: Chronic illnesses with extremely slow recovery and restlessness. Difficult and persistent diseases. Maladies caused by damp and cold pathogens. Obstructive disorders. Extreme vacuity of kidney *jing*.

Specific Indications: Generalized paralysis due to damp pathogenic factors. Immobility of the lower back due to pain. Kidney yang vacuity due to sexual excess. Exterior cold and interior heat. Vomiting. Indigestion. Tumors of internal organs.

Moving lines

Line 1: Going leads to obstruction. Coming leads to honor.

Fair prognosis. Stagnation of qi and blood in the abdomen. Gastric distress. Diarrhea. Bleeding. Epistaxis. Foot pain. Fever.

Line 2: The imperial servants are severely obstructed, but they are not at fault.

Fair prognosis. Spastic pain in the legs. Wind diseases. Flu.

Line 3: Going leads to obstruction. One, therefore, will return.

Fair prognosis. Abdominal pain. Kidney dysfunction. Kidney *jing* vacuity. Sexual weakness. Lower back pain. Painful stagnation of qi and blood in the abdomen.

Line 4: Going leads to obstruction. Coming leads to association.

Poor prognosis. Lung diseases. Flu. Kidney *jing* vacuity. Sexual weakness. Spermatorrhea. Hypersensitivity of the nerves.

Line 5: In the middle of a severe obstruction, friends will come.

Poor prognosis. Spleen and kidney vacuity. Blood stasis. Vertigo. Weak limbs.

Line 6: Going leads to obstruction. Coming leads to great good fortune. One should see the great person.

Good prognosis. Headaches. Fever.

40. *Jie (Hsieh)*, Deliverance

Thunder and rain start,
The image of *Jie*.
The superior person thus pardons mistakes
   and forgives misconduct.

The Judgement: *Jie* means that one should go southwest. If there is no place to go, coming back brings good fortune. If there is a place to go, rushing brings good fortune.

General Indications: Deliverance from chronic illnesses. Dispersion of internal toxins toward the exterior surface. Release of obstruction or blockage by surgery.

Specific Indications: Disharmony between the qi and blood. Sore throat from excessive coughing. Vomiting. Heat in the stomach. Food stagnation. Abdominal pains. Genital sores. Seizures. Postpartum blood stasis.

Moving lines

Line 1: No blame.

Fair prognosis. Blood vacuity. Damp heat in the bladder. Cystitis with frequency and urgency. Anuria. Venereal diseases. Abdominal tumors. Joint pain. Cold limbs.

Line 2: One takes three foxes in the field and receives three yellow arrows. Perseverance brings good fortune.

Fair prognosis. Spleen and stomach qi vacuity. Digestive distress. Kidney *jing* vacuity. Painful bowel movement. Nervous breakdown.

142

Line 3: If one carries a load on their back and yet rides in a carriage, they will invite robbers. Perseverance brings humiliation.

Fair prognosis. Food poisoning. Severe vomiting. Epigastric spasms due to qi stagnation. Injury by wind. Lower back pain.

Line 4: Cut off your big toes. Then your friends will come. You can trust them.

Fair prognosis. Kidney vacuity. Damp heat in the stomach. Jaundice. Injury by wind. Paralysis from stroke. Syphilis. Severe blood stasis. Blood vacuity.

Line 5: Only the superior person can settle the situation. There will be good fortune. One thus demonstrates their compassion to the inferior.

Fair prognosis. Severe headaches. Subcostal pain. Nervous breakdown.

Line 6: The prince shoots at a hawk on a high castle wall and kills it. Everything improves.

Good prognosis. Fever and chills. Headaches. Vertigo.

41. *Sun (Sun)*, Decrease

The marsh at the foot of the mountain,
The image of *Sun*.
The superior person thus contains their resentment
   and curbs their desires.

The Judgement: *Sun* means that being sincere brings supreme good fortune. There is no blame in this. Be patient. One should undertake something. How can this be done? Offer two bowls in sacrifice.

General Indications: Diminished state of health. Chronic exhaustion. Mental and emotional fatigue leading to depression and pessimism.

Specific Indications: Fatigue from excessive stress. Nervous breakdown. Debility from sexual excess. Lung disease. Flushing-up. Anorexia. Menstrual irregularities. Blood vacuity.

Moving lines

Line 1: Leave as soon as your work is done. There is no blame in this. Reflect on how much work you can reduce by this.

Fair prognosis. Severe diarrhea. Bleeding. Epistaxis. Boils. Foot pain. Eye diseases. Earache. Severe abdominal pains.

Line 2: Perseverance brings good fortune. Going on like this will bring misfortune. One can thus augment others without depleting oneself.

Fair prognosis. Headaches with fever. Nausea. Epigastric spasm from food stagnation. Gum problems. Toothache. Diseases of the oral cavity.

144

Line 3: If three people travel together, they will lose one person. If a person travels by themself, they will gain friends.

Fair prognosis. Left abdominal mass. Lower back pain due to cold. Food stagnation. Amenorrhoea with blood stasis. Abdominal distention.

Line 4: If a person can minimize their shortcomings, others will quickly join them to rejoice. There is no blame in this.

Fair prognosis. Chest pain from blood and phlegm stagnation. Fever. Breathing difficulty.

Line 5: Somebody did augment one. Ten pairs of tortoises cannot contest this. There will be supreme good fortune.

Poor prognosis. Collapse of yin with high fever. Severe headaches. Arrhythmia. Severe prostration.

Line 6: If one can augment oneself without diminishing others, there is no blame in this. Perseverance brings good fortune. One should undertake something. One may obtain servants, but may lose one's house.

Fair prognosis. Qi vacuity. Mental stress from severe qi vacuity. Headaches.

42. *Yi (I)*, Increase

Wind and thunder,
The image of *Yi*.
Thus the superior person emulates a good person when one
  sees one.
If one has faults,
One is quick to correct them.

The Judgement: *Yi* means that one should undertake
something. One should cross the great river.

General Indications: Problems due to spleen vacuity and liver
wind. Qi stagnation. Brain dysfunction. Menstrual problems.

Specific Indications: Qi flushing up to the heart. Indigestion.
Food stagnation. Contagious viral diseases. Nervous breakdown.
Amnesia. Mental retardation. Hemorrhoids. Vaginal discharge.

Moving lines

Line 1: One should undertake a great project. There will be
supreme great fortune. No blame.

Fair prognosis. Qi rebelling up to the head. Fever. Vertigo.
Severe diarrhea with abdominal pain. Viral infections. Breathing
difficulty. Generalized arthralgia. Paralysis.

Line 2: Somebody has augmented one. Ten pairs of tortoises
cannot contest this. Continuous perseverance brings good
fortune. The king will present one to the emperor. There will be
good fortune.

146

Fair prognosis. Febrile diseases. Lung ailments. Arrhythmia. Burning pain in the throat. Phlegm stagnation in the lungs. Leg pain.

Line 3: One is augmented through an inauspicious event. There will be no blame in this. If one is sincere and moderate, one will report to the king with a seal.

Fair prognosis. Subcostal spasm due to liver wind. Stomach qi vacuity. Wind eye. Meningitis. Anorexia. Constipation. Anuria. Grave febrile diseases.

Line 4: If one is moderate and report to the king, he will listen to you. One should be involved in relocating the capital of the government.

Fair prognosis. Palpitations. Qi stagnation in the epigastrium. Spastic pain of the lower back. Mental depression.

Line 5: If one is sincere and compassionate, do not ask any question. There will be supreme good fortune. One's sincerity bolsters one's character.

Good prognosis. Febrile illnesses. Injury from cold. Indigestion. Paralysis.

Line 6: One has not augmented anyone. Some people even have struck them. One's intentions are not consistent. There will be misfortune.

Poor prognosis. Alternating fever and cold. Excessive stagnation of fluids all over the body. Edema. Headaches. Loss of hearing. Degeneration of vision.

43. *Guai (Kuai)*, Breakthrough (Resoluteness)

The marsh above heaven,
The image of *Guai*.
The superior person thus awards their subordinates
    and abhors to keep their merits to themself.

The Judgement: *Guai* means one must announce the situation at the imperial court. Although the true declaration will bring danger, one must notify their own townspeople. One should not resort to arms. One should have a place to go.

General Indications: Severe illnesses. Respiratory diseases. Brain derangement. Mental and emotional disorders. Skin problems. Traumatic illnesses.

Specific Indications: Phlegm in the lungs. Subcostal spasms from the liver qi stagnation. Fluid stagnation causing eczema. Fungal infection of the skin. Mental depression and confusion. Trauma to the head. Rebellious qi attacking the heart.

Moving lines

Line 1: Powerful progress in the toes. Going like this is a mistake.

Poor prognosis. Collapse of the *shen*. Mental diseases. Nausea and vomiting. Edema. Trauma to the foot. Clotty menstruation.

Line 2: Shouts of alarm. There are enemies in the evening and at night. Be vigilant.

Fair prognosis. Seasonal cold with fever. Constipation. Anuria. Heat phlegm in the lungs. Severe headaches.

148

Line 3: Being powerful in cheekbones brings misfortune. The superior person is firmly determined to go alone and is caught in the rain. They are wet and angry. But there is no blame in this.

Fair prognosis. Kidney *jing* vacuity. Asthma with phlegm. Latent fever. Epilepsy. Mental derangement. Lower back pain. Problems of oral cavity.

Line 4: There is no skin on one's buttocks and one cannot walk well. If one allows themself to be led like a sheep, remorse will disappear. Even if one speaks, one will not be believed.

Fair prognosis. Cold and damp conditions. Food stagnation. Abdominal pain. Boils on the buttocks. Hemorrhoids. Venereal diseases. Gonorrhea.

Line 5: Weeds in the marsh are very strong. Moderation is free from blame.

Fair prognosis. Liver wind rebelling up to the head. Mental confusion. Chest pain. Hysteria.

Line 6: No more alarm. There will be misfortune in the end.

Poor prognosis. Collapse of *shen*. Mental derangement. Severe headaches. Brain tumor with mental confusion. Systemic edema. Inability to eat. Dyspnea.

44. *Gou (Kou)*, Coming to Meet

Wind blows under heaven,
The image of *Gou*.
The prince thus disseminates his orders
   in all directions of the world.

The Judgement: *Gou* means the woman is powerful and one should not marry such a woman.

General Indications: Yin vacuity and yang repletion. Vacuity heat rising to the upper body. Hormonal imbalances. Mental stress. Indigestion. Slow onset of an illness but rapid changes later.

Specific Indications: Cold with fever and headaches. Lack of appetite with food stagnation. Facial edema. Nervous breakdown. Impotence. Anal prolapse. Postpartum complications. Uterine problems.

Moving lines

Line 1: It must be fastened to a metal pole. Perseverance brings good fortune. Undertaking brings misfortune. Even a lean pig has courage to move around.

Fair prognosis. Kidney *jing* vacuity. Exhaustion. Constipation. Dysuria. Foot pain. Cold.

Line 2: There is a fish in the tank. There is no blame in this. One should have a guest.

Fair prognosis. Hemorrhoids. Leg pain. Diarrhea with damp heat in the intestines.

150

Line 3: There is no skin on one's buttocks and one cannot walk well. If one is aware of possible danger, they will not make a great mistake.

Fair prognosis. Bleeding disorders. Diarrhea. Venereal diseases. Lower back pain due to cold stagnation. Severe hemorrhoids.

Line 4: There are no fish in the tank. Rising brings misfortune.

Poor prognosis. Profound yin vacuity. Kidney *jing* vacuity. Wind paralysis. Emaciation. Stroke.

Line 5: The mellon is wrapped with willow leaves. The talent is hidden. It is the one fallen from heaven.

Fair prognosis. Fever. Qi flushing up to the head. Weakening of vision. Headaches.

Line 6: He comes to meet her with passion. This will bring humiliation, but there is no blame in this.

Poor prognosis. Severe headaches. Chest congestion with phlegm. Generalized edema. Abdominal distention from stagnation.

45. *Cui (Ts'ui)*, Gathering Together (Massing)

A marsh on the earth,
The image of *Cui*.
The superior person thus abandons their weapons
and prevents disorders.

The Judgement: *Cui* means that the king arrives at his ancestral temple and, therefore, one should see the great person. Perseverance brings success. To offer a great sacrifice brings good fortune. One should undertake something.

General Indications: Accumulation of toxins. Overstressed digestive system from food stagnation. *Wei qi* vacuity. Weakness of the immune system from toxic congestion. Dampness congesting the system. Two concurrent pathologies.

Specific Indications: Food poisoning. Food stagnation. Gastro-intestinal cancer. Lung congestion with coughing. Vomiting. Diarrhea. Hysteria.

Moving lines

Line 1: Although one is sincere, one cannot work things through to the end. There will sometimes be confusion and sometimes gathering of people. If one calls out for help, one can laugh again after one shaking of the hands. Do not be afraid. Going is without blame.

Fair prognosis. Spleen vacuity. Liver qi flushing to the head. Spastic pain in the feet and the legs. Arrhythmia.

Line 2: If one lets others guide them, one will have good fortune and be blameless. If one is sincere, one will bring a small offering.

152

Fair prognosis. Qi vacuity. Kidney *jing* vacuity. Impotence. Venereal diseases. Diarrhea. Lower back pain due to cold stagnation.

Line 3: People gather together and deplore. Nothing should be undertaken. Going is without blame but will bring slight humiliation.

Fair prognosis. Depression from loss of love. Nervous breakdown. Lung diseases. Injury from cold.

Line 4: Great good fortune. No blame.

Fair prognosis. Kidney and spleen vacuity. Subcostal pain from qi stagnation. Illnesses from internal causation (imbalance of the seven emotions, incorrect diet, sexual excess, etc.).

Line 5: People gather around a person with a high rank. There is no blame in this. This is not because of sincerity. Continuous perseverance dissipates remorse.

Poor prognosis. Chronic spleen and kidney vacuity. Food poisoning. Gastrointestinal cancers. Vomiting.

Line 6: Lamenting and mourning, there will be floods of tears. There is no blame in this.

Fair prognosis. Qi stagnation under the ribs. Headaches. Vertigo. Subcostal pain.

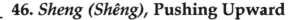

46. *Sheng (Shêng)*, **Pushing Upward**

The tree grows in the soil,
The image of *Sheng*.
Thus the superior person cultivates their character.
By accumulating small merits,
    they accomplish something high and great.

The Judgement: *Sheng* means supreme success. One should see the great person. Do not be afraid. Going south brings good fortune.

General Indications: Upward movement of qi and blood to the head, causing congestion and stagnation. Gastrointestinal distress. Fast shift in symptomatology.

Specific Indications: Seizures. Vertigo. Headaches. Stroke. Mental derangement. Meningitis. Food stagnation. Abdominal mass. Vomiting. Diarrhea.

Moving lines

Line 1: Pushing upward with confidence brings good fortune.

Fair prognosis. Spleen vacuity leading to indigestion, constipation, cold extremities, and fatigue. Kidney *jing* vacuity. Blood stasis in the lower abdomen.

Line 2: If one is sincere, one should bring a small offering. There is no blame in this.

Fair prognosis. Leg pains. General paralysis. Exhaustion. Kidney *jing* vacuity. Lower back pain.

Line 3: One pushes upward into an empty village.

154

Fair prognosis. Damp heat in the stomach. Constipation. Bleeding hemorrhoids. Lower back pain. Menstrual irregularities from blood vacuity. Vaginal discharge.

Line 4: The king appoints one to Mount Qi. There will be good fortune. There is no blame in this.

Fair prognosis. Abdominal pain with distention from deep qi and blood stagnation.

Line 5: Perseverance brings good fortune. One pushes upward by the stairs.

Poor prognosis. Heat in the heart. Chest pains. Hearing loss. Lung diseases. Nervous breakdown.

Line 6: One pushes up into the darkness. One should seriously persevere.

Fair prognosis. Water stagnation. Headaches. Stiff shoulders. Boils. Edema. Traumatic injury.

47. *Kun (K'un)*, Oppression (Exhaustion)

No water in the lake,
The image of *Kun*.
The superior person thus accomplishes their mission
　by carrying out their will.

The Judgement: *Kun* means that the great person should be persevering. This brings good fortune. There is no blame in this. Even though one has something to say, they will not be believed.

General Indications: Debilitation from yin and yang vacuity. Prolonged, difficult illnesses. Inability to recover from a disease. May require hospitalization.

Specific Indications: Kidney and spleen vacuity. Emaciation. Insomnia. Anorexia. Vomiting. Bleeding. Spermatorrhea. Hemorrhoids. Venereal diseases. Death by drowning.

Moving lines

Line 1: One's buttocks hurt when one sat on a tree stump. Then they walked into a dark valley. One will not be seen for three years.

Fair prognosis. Dysuria. Stubborn cough with phlegm. Pains in the buttocks. Foot pains. Joint pains. Boils on the hip. Toothache. Ear problem. Vaginal discharge.

Line 2: One suffers at a banquet. The man with the scarlet knee band is soon coming. One should offer a sacrifice. Going forth brings misfortune, but there is no blame in this.

Fair prognosis. Spleen qi vacuity. Food poisoning. Abdominal pains. Leg pains. Kidney *jing* vacuity.

Line 3: One is hurt by stone and is leaning on thorns and thistles. Even though one enters their house, they do not see their wife. There will be misfortune.

Fair prognosis. Trauma to the abdomen. Food stagnation causing abdominal distention. Constipation. Edema of legs. Injury by cold. Eye diseases. Ear infections.

Line 4: One came very slowly, stuck in a golden carriage. There will be misfortune. The end has come.

Poor prognosis. Cardiac problems. Kidney failure. Severe diarrhea with bleeding. Nervous breakdown. Vomiting of blood. Severe venereal diseases.

Line 5: One's nose and feet are cut off. One is tortured by the man with the red knee bands. Joy will come very slowly. One should offer a sacrifice.

Fair prognosis. Liver wind rising to the head. Asthma. Fatigue. Epilepsy. Stiff shoulders.

Line 6: One is stuck in the creeping ivy. This makes one apprehensive. One says to oneself, "If I move, I will regret it." But, if one regrets it and moves, one will have good fortune.

Fair prognosis. Stiff shoulders. Boils. Edema.

48. *Jing (Ching)*, The Well

There is water on the tree,
The image of *Jing*.
The superior person thus urges people to work hard
     and advises them to help each other.

The Judgement: *Jing* means that the village can be moved, but the well cannot be moved. It is neither lost nor obtained. People can come and go to draw from the well. If one lowers the rope almost to the water, and it does not go all the way or the jug breaks, it will bring misfortune.

General Indications: *Yuan qi* vacuity. Debilitating mental illnesses. Cold, damp diseases. Toxic conditions.

Specific Indications: Lung diseases. Boils. Joint pains. Chest pains. Diarrhea. Ear infection. Vaginal discharge.

Moving lines

Line 1: The muddy well cannot be drawn. An old well invites no animals.

Fair prognosis. Food stagnation. Insomnia. Goiter. Diabetes. Arthritis. Anal prolapse. Venereal diseases. Edema. Leg pain. Tetanus.

Line 2: Only carp stay at the well hole. The jug is broken and it leaks.

Fair prognosis. Subcostal pain. Liver qi rising to the head. Hysteria. Muscle spasm in the shoulders. Lower back pain. Venereal disease. Tetanus. Inability to move about.

158

Line 3: The well is cleared but water is not drawn. It breaks my heart, because it can be used. If the king is bright, his fortune may be shared in common.

Fair prognosis. Diarrhea. Boils. Mental depression. Illnesses due to dampness. Edema.

Line 4: The well is repaired. There is no blame in this.

Fair prognosis. Dyspnea. Asthma due to phlegm stagnation. Ascites. Severe vomiting and diarrhea. Clotty menstruation. Heat in the stomach. Liver wind rising to the heart.

Line 5: The well is filled with a clear, cold spring. The water can be drunk.

Poor prognosis. Severe degeneration of vision. Tinnitus. Headaches with vertigo. Paralysis. Congenital syphilis.

Line 6: The well can be drawn without restraint. If one is sincere, one will have supreme good fortune.

Fair prognosis. Complications of cold or flu. Arrhythmias. Headaches. General prostration.

49. *Ge (Ko)*, Revolution (Molting)

Fire in the marsh,
The image of *Ge*.
Thus the superior person sets the calendar in order
and defines the timetable.

The Judgement: *Ge* means that one will be recognized on the day of their accomplishment. There will be supreme success. Perseverance brings progress. Remorse disappears.

General Indications: Sudden and complete change in symptomatology. Aggressive and changeable illnesses. Febrile diseases. Diseases with yin and yang disharmony. Blood vacuity. Contagious illnesses. Unusual diseases. Sudden death.

Specific Indications: Lung diseases with fever and phlegm. Bleeding disorders. Flu and cold. Constipation from heat in the intestines. Hoarseness.

Moving lines

Line 1: One is wrapped up with yellow cow hide.

Fair prognosis. Damp heat. Abscess of internal organs. Kidney *jing* vacuity. Injury by cold. Flu. Jaundice. Painful paralysis of the limbs.

Line 2: When one's day comes, one will be able to carry out a revolution. Starting brings good fortune. There is no blame in this.

Fair prognosis. Abdominal distention due to heat stagnation. Liver qi rising to the head. Constipation. Cough with phlegm. Dysentery.

160

Line 3: Starting brings good fortune. Perseverance brings misfortune. When the plan of revolution goes around three times, one may commit oneself to it, and people will believe one.

Fair prognosis. Pains from food stagnation. Vomiting. Mental confusion. Venereal diseases.

Line 4: Remorse disappears. People believe one. A revolution brings good fortune.

Fair prognosis. Severe blood and qi vacuity. Sharp subcostal pains due to liver wind. Lung dysfunction. Abdominal pains. Boils.

Line 5: The great person changes like a tiger. Even before they cast the oracle, they are believed.

Fair prognosis. High fever. Qi vacuity. Chest pains. Back pains.

Line 6: The superior person changes like a panther. The inferior person only changes their face. Starting brings misfortune. To remain firm brings good fortune.

Fair prognosis. Severe headaches with fever. Seasonal cold and flu.

50. *Ding (Ting)*, The Cauldron

Fire over wood,
The image of *Ding*.
The superior person thus carries out their mission
    by correcting their attitude.

The Judgement: *Ding* means supreme good fortune. There will be success.

General Indications: Diseases due to excessive diet, emotional indulgence, and sexual excess. Powerful and virulent illnesses. Liver yang repletion. Infections from food.

Specific Indications: Contagious febrile illnesses. Mental dysfunction. Boils. Lung diseases. Generalized edema. Cystitis. Constipation. Pregnancy.

Moving lines

Line 1: The cauldron is placed upside down. One should thus get rid of harmful substances. He takes a concubine for the sake of her son. There is no blame in this.

Fair prognosis. Subcostal pains due to liver wind. Vomiting and abdominal distention due to excessive diet. Constipation. Edema. Gait problems.

Line 2: There is some food in the cauldron. My companions are jealous of it, but they cannot hurt me. There will be good fortune.

Poor prognosis. Phlegm misting the portals of the heart. Heavy limbs. Poor elimination. Paralysis of the legs.

162

Line 3: The handles of the cauldron are transformed. One's path is thus blocked. The grease of the pheasant should not be eaten. Once it rains, the remorse will disappear. There will be good fortune in the end.

Fair prognosis. Damp heat in the bladder. Severe diarrhea. Lower back pain. Hemorrhoids. Venereal diseases.

Line 4: The legs of the cauldron are broken. The meal of the prince is spilt and his person is soiled. There will be misfortune.

Poor prognosis. Violent seizures. Heart attack. Severe rebelling of the liver qi.

Line 5: The cauldron has yellow handles and golden strings. Perseverance brings good fortune.

Fair prognosis. Subcostal pain due to liver qi stagnation. Cough. Edema. High fever. Weakening of vision. Tinnitus.

Line 6: The rings of the cauldron are made of jade. There will be great good fortune. Everything improves.

Good prognosis. Seizures. Headaches. Liver qi stagnation. Vision disturbances.

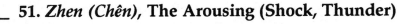

51. *Zhen (Chên)*, The Arousing (Shock, Thunder)

Thunder repeated,
The image of *Zhen*.
The superior person thus corrects themself
    through introspection.

The Judgement: *Zhen* means success. Thunder comes with "Oh, oh!" Laughing words are "Ha, ha!" The thunder can shock a hundred miles, but the man will not drop the sacred ladle and chalice.

General Indications: An illness with sudden onset. Aggressive diseases. Severe pains. Constantly changing symptoms. Liver conquering the spleen. Fits and seizures. Spasms.

Specific Indications: Epileptic attacks. Mental illnesses. Frenzied state of mind. Vertigo. Ear diseases. Insomnia. Muscle sprain. Intermittent fever. Hysteria. Birth of twins.

Moving lines

Line 1: First, thunder comes with "Oh, oh!" Then, laughing comes with "Ha, ha!" There will be good fortune.

Fair prognosis. Acute abdominal pain. Liver qi rebelling up to the heart. Stroke. Painful paralysis of lower legs.

Line 2: Thunder comes with danger. It comes a hundred thousand times. Even if one loses one's treasures and has to climb nine hills, do not go looking for them. You will get them back in seven days.

Fair prognosis. Chest pain with cough. Abdominal pain. Liver qi rising to the heart. Cold legs. Joint pains. Stroke. Mental depression.

Line 3: Thunder comes and makes one feel petrified. If the shock pushes one into action, one will remain blameless.

Fair prognosis. Acute high fever. Manic state. Acute venereal diseases. Clotty menses.

Line 4: Thunder has fallen to the ground.

Fair prognosis. Deep qi and blood stagnation. Severe subcostal pain. Painful spasms of the limbs. *Jing* vacuity. Exhaustion. Intermittent abdominal pains.

Line 5: Thunder comes and goes. Danger, yet nothing is lost. And there still is something to do.

Fair prognosis. Dyspnea with severe chest pain. Vomiting. Angina pectoris.

Line 6: Thunder brings ruin. It is a terrifying scene to see. Going ahead brings misfortune. If it has not harmed one's body and has not reached one's neighbors, there is no blame in it. One's friend will have something to talk about.

Poor prognosis. Coma. Heart attack. Mental delusion. Headaches. Degeneration of vision. Severe toothache.

52. *Gen (Kên)*, Keeping Still (Mountain)

Mountain repeated,
The image of *Gen*.
The superior person thus does not go beyond
   their limitations.

The Judgement: *Gen* means that one keeps their back still so that one does not feel their body at all. Although one enters their courtyard, one does not see their people. There is no blame in this.

General Indications: Chronic state of an illness. Unchangeable symptomatology. Swelling from fluid stagnation. Congested state. Trauma. Paralysis.

Specific Indications: Poor circulation. Nervous breakdown. Spleen vacuity causing food stagnation and diarrhea. Stubborn joint pains. Stroke. Boils. Menstrual congestion.

Moving lines

Line 1: One keeps their toes still. There is no blame in this. One should persevere constantly.

Fair prognosis with prompt treatment. Fever. Liver yang rising. Spleen/stomach disharmony. Diarrhea. Bleeding disorders. Head congestion. Edema.

Line 2: One keeps their calves still. One cannot save the man that one is following. Thus, one's heart is not content.

Fair prognosis. Arthritis of the legs. Heart pain. Boils from toxins. Paralysis of the lower legs. Fits of children.

Line 3: One keeps their hips still, making their lower back stiff. There may be danger. Then, one's heart will suffer.

Fair prognosis. Kidney vacuity. Lower back pain. Venereal diseases. Heart diseases. Difficulty in walking from leg paralysis. Inability to eat.

Line 4: One keeps their trunk still. There is no blame in this.

Fair prognosis. Chest pain. Stubborn, latent fevers. Qi flushing up. Emotional depression. Persistent subcostal pain.

Line 5: One keeps their jaws still. Since one keeps one's words in order, remorse disappears.

Poor prognosis. Dyspnea. Painful spasms of the limbs. Paralysis. Painful stagnation of qi.

Line 6: One is good at keeping oneself still. There will be good fortune.

Poor prognosis. Severe vacuity of the kidneys and spleen. Disharmony of the qi and blood. Shoulder pain. Paralysis. Boils.

53. *Jian (Chien)*, Development (Gradual Progress)

There are trees on the mountain,
The image of *Jian*.
Thus the superior person improves the public
   by abiding in dignity and in virtue.

The Judgement: *Jian* means that it is good fortune for a woman to be married. She should persevere.

General Indications: Gradual, progressive diseases with slow onset. Continual changes of symptomatology. Death.

Specific Indications: Intensifying depression. Progressive cold. Food poisoning. Stomach pain with subcostal qi stagnation.

Moving lines

Line 1: The great wild goose gradually approaches the shore. Its young son is in danger. There is some gossip. There is no blame in this.

Fair prognosis. Leg pain. Injury by cold. Depression. Constipation.

Line 2: The great wild goose gradually approaches the cliff. It eats and drinks in peace. There will be good fortune.

Fair prognosis. Severe cold. Foot pain. Fluid stagnation. Edema.

Line 3: The great wild goose gradually approaches the land. The man went to war but has not returned. The woman begot a child but did not raise it. There will be misfortune. One should fight robbers off.

168

Fair prognosis. Disharmony of the qi and blood. Liver qi rising to the head. Vertigo. Headaches. Liver conquering the spleen. Paralysis.

Line 4: The great wild goose gradually approaches the tree. It may find a flat branch.

Good prognosis. Abdominal distention from food poisoning. Depression. Injury by cold. Subcostal spasm from liver qi stagnation.

Line 5: The great wild goose gradually approaches the summit. The woman will not have a child for three years, but, in the end, she will not be hindered. There will be good fortune.

Fair prognosis. Blood stagnation. Chest pains. Breast cancer. Stomach problems of children. Amenorrhea. Stroke. Boils on the back.

Line 6: The great wild goose gradually approaches the clouds. Its feathers can be used for the holy dance. There will be good fortune.

Fair prognosis. Vomiting. Abdominal abscesses. Severe indigestion. Eye diseases. Ear infections. Pain in the shoulder and the neck. Boils.

54. *Gui Mei (Kuei Mei)*, **The Marrying Maiden**

Thunder over the marsh,
The image of *Gui Mei*.
The superior person thus knows the transitoriness of things
in the light of what is eternal.

The Judgement: *Gui Mei* means that going ahead will bring misfortune. Nothing improves.

General Indications: Illnesses from emotional, sexual, and dietary overindulgence. Liver yang repletion. Excessive mental strain. Drug abuse. Death.

Specific Indications: Emotional breakdown. Sexual excess. Compulsive overeating. Excessive anger. Hysteria. Dyspnea with phlegm. Venereal diseases. Leg edema. Drug allergy.

Moving lines

Line 1: The woman enters the marriage as a concubine. She is like a lame person who cannot walk too well. Going ahead brings good fortune.

Good prognosis. Pain in lower extremities from cold stagnation. Boils. Diarrhea. Bleeding. Sore throat.

Line 2: The woman is like a cross-eyed person who cannot see too well. One should persevere like a hermit.

Fair prognosis. Severe liver wind repletion. Qi flushing up. Leg spasms. Paranoic anxiety. Diseases of the oral cavity. Meningitis in children. Phobias.

Line 3: The woman is like a slave. She marries as a concubine.

170

Fair prognosis. Leg pain due to cold. Liver wind repletion. Acute contagious illnesses. Edema. Generalized muscle spasm. Sexual excess. Compulsive overeating. Venereal diseases.

Line 4: The woman missed the right time to marry, but she will eventually get married.

Fair prognosis. *Jing* vacuity. Painful paralysis of foot due to cold. Nervous breakdown.

Line 5: The Emperor Yi gave his daughter in marriage. Her attire was not as beautiful as the concubine's. The moon is nearly full. There will be good fortune.

Fair prognosis. Chest pains with phlegm. Dyspnea. Subcostal spasms.

Line 6: The woman receives a chest in which there is no treasure. The man stabs the sheep, but no blood flows. Nothing improves.

Fair prognosis. High fever. Headaches. Palpitations. Heat blisters in the mouth. Constipation.

55. *Feng (Fêng)*, Abundance (Fullness)

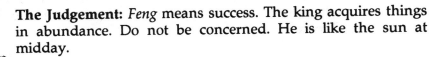

Thunder and lightning come together,
The image of *Feng*.
Thus the superior person settles litigation
   and executes justice.

The Judgement: *Feng* means success. The king acquires things in abundance. Do not be concerned. He is like the sun at midday.

General Indications: Acute febrile diseases. Dynamic symptomatic changes with pain. Liver yang repletion. Sexual overindulgence. Eye diseases. Pregnancy.

Specific Indications: Flu and cold with high fever. Liver yang disturbing the heart. Kidney yang vacuity. Adolescent tuberculosis. Senile dementia.

Moving lines

Line 1: The man meets his destined master and he stays with him for ten days. There is no mistake in this. Going ahead gains recognition.

Fair prognosis. Blood stasis. Cardiac distress. Poor circulation. Foot pain. Leg paralysis.

Line 2: The shutters are so thick that the polestar can been seen at noon. If one goes, one will meet with mistrust and hate. If one follows their inner truth, one will meet with good fortune.

Fair prognosis. Eye diseases. Vertigo. Mental confusion. Boils. Lung diseases. Abdominal distention. Edema of the lower extremities. Joint pains.

Line 3: The curtains are so thick that small stars can be seen at noon. One breaks their right arm. There is no fault in this.

Fair prognosis. *Jing* vacuity. Acute contagious diseases. Liver yang repletion. Lower back pain. Intestinal gas. Bone fracture.

Line 4: The shutters are so thick that the polestar can be seen at noon. The man meets with his master of like kind. There will be good fortune.

Poor prognosis. Cardiac arrest. Mental derangement. Pains from damp heat in the stomach. Jaundice. Malignant tumors of the skin. Paralysis. Blindness.

Line 5: Brightness is coming. There is blessing and fame in it. Good fortune.

Fair prognosis. Lung qi vacuity. Dyspnea. Subcostal pain. Excessive phlegm.

Line 6: One's house is extremely luxurious and the curtains shutter the family off. One peeps through the gate and sees no one. For three years, nobody is seen. There will be misfortune.

Poor prognosis. Coma. Arrhythmia. High fever. Headaches. Unconsciousness. Death.

56. *Lu (Lü)*, The Wanderer

There is fire on the mountain,
The image of *Lu*.
The superior person thus is bright and careful
   in imposing penalties.
They would not prolong any litigation.

The Judgement: *Lu* means small success. Perseverance brings good fortune to the traveller.

General Indications: Illnesses of migrating nature. Contagious diseases contracted during travelling. Emotional strains.

Specific Indications: Food poisoning. Dysentery. Mental depression. Liver yang repletion. Stroke. Blood stasis. Impaired vision. Irregular menstruation. Postpartum anemia.

Moving lines

Line 1: If the traveller timidly hurries themself, they will invite misfortune upon themself.

Fair prognosis. Damp heat. Dysentery. Food poisoning. Cystitis. Nephritis. Severe foot pain. Edema.

Line 2: The traveller arrives at an inn. One has plenty of funds. One also finds a young servant. Be firm.

Fair prognosis. Liver wind rebelling up. Injury by cold with fever and headaches. Food stagnation. Foot pain. Edema.

Line 3: The traveller's inn burns down. One loses their young servant. Perseverance brings danger.

Poor prognosis. Liver yang repletion. Dysentery. Mental derangement. Eye problems. Boils. Severe blood vacuity.

Line 4: The traveller rests at a shelter. One obtains one's funds and an ax. My heart is not happy.

Fair prognosis. Severe emotional and mental stress. Food stagnation. Chest pain. Lower back pain. Paralysis.

Line 5: One shoots a pheasant. It is taken with one arrow. There will be honor and position in the end.

Fair prognosis. Lung congestion with phlegm. Headaches. Severe eye disease. Joint pains.

Line 6: The bird burns its nest. At first, the traveller laughs. Then, they weep loudly. One also loses their cow on the border. There will be misfortune.

Fair prognosis. Qi stagnation. Hepatic diseases. Headaches. Food poisoning.

57. *Sun (Sun)*, The Gentle (The Penetrating, Wind)

Wind follows wind,
The image of *Sun*.
The superior person thus spreads their command
and execute their ventures.

The Judgement: *Sun* means small success. One should undertake something. One should see the great person.

General Indications: Chronic moderate diseases with subtle symptomatology. Problems from the wind pathogenic factor. Contagious diseases. Acute pains of migrating nature.

Specific Indications: Lung diseases. Depression due to qi vacuity. Injury from cold. Flu. Stroke. Rectal diseases. Boils. Joint pains. Diseases of genitalia. Viral infections.

Moving lines

Line 1: One advances, then one retreats. One should persevere like a warrior.

Fair prognosis. Alternating symptoms. Cough with phlegm. Painful paralysis of the lower extremities. Fluid stagnation in the lower extremities.

Line 2: Gentleness at the foot of the bed. One employs priests and magicians in great number. There will be good fortune. No blame.

Fair prognosis. Lung diseases from wind injury. Viral infections. Depression from qi stagnation. Joint pains. Problems of the genitalia.

176

Line 3: One tries to influence others too frequently. There will be humiliation.

Fair prognosis. Lower back pain due to cold stagnation and wind. Diarrhea. Venereal diseases. Sexual excess. Irregular menses.

Line 4: Remorse disappears. One took three kinds of game during the hunt.

Fair prognosis. Food stagnation. Dysentery. Abdominal muscle spasms. Swelling of the breast. Bronchitis.

Line 5: Perseverance brings good fortune. Remorse disappears. Everything improves. There is no beginning but an end. Before the change, three days. After the change, three days. There will be good fortune.

Fair prognosis. Food poisoning. Food stagnation. Boils. Parasitic infestations.

Line 6: Gentleness at the foot of the bed. One loses their funds and their ax. Perseverance brings misfortune.

Poor prognosis. Vomiting of blood. Stroke. Tuberculosis. Brain tumor.

58. *Dui (Tui)*, The Lake

A marsh over a marsh,
The image of *Dui*.
Thus the superior person joins their friends
    to teach and to learn.

The Judgement: *Dui* means success. One should persevere.

General Indications: Chronic slow diseases. Toxic conditions. Lung diseases. Sexual overstimulation. Venereal diseases. Digestive problems.

Specific Indications: Kidney yang vacuity. Food stagnation. Tuberculosis. Asthma. Pain in the mouth. Epilepsy. Vaginitis. Menstrual irregularities.

Moving lines

Line 1: The joy of harmony. There will be good fortune.

Fair prognosis. Spleen vacuity. Diarrhea. Lung congestion. Sexual excess.

Line 2: The joy of sincerity. There will be good fortune. Remorse disappears.

Fair prognosis. Phlegm stagnation. Lower abdominal distention and muscle spasm. Poor urination.

Line 3: The joy of coming. There will be misfortune.

Poor prognosis. Kidney failure. Vertigo. Dyspnea. Lower back pain. Postpartum uterine inflammation.

Line 4: Joy through manipulation has no peace. If one can correct their mistakes, one will have joy.

Fair prognosis. Injury from cold. Vomiting of blood. Stomach distress. Joint pains.

Line 5: One is exploited by being sincere. There may be danger.

Fair prognosis. Liver yang repletion. Heat in the stomach. Food stagnation. Chest pain with palpitations.

Line 6: Joy through attraction.

Fair prognosis. Swelling of the mouth. Headaches. Injury from cold.

59. *Huan (Huan)*, Dispersion (Dissolution)

Wind blows on the water,
The image of *Huan*.
The kings offered sacrifice at their ancestral temples.

The Judgement: The king approaches his temple. One should cross the great river. Perseverance is advantageous.

General Indications: Disappearance of symptoms. Diseases due to cold damp pathogenic factors. Sudden death.

Specific Indications: Stomachache. Food poisoning. Diarrhea. Kidney problems. Arthritis. Lower back pain. Hemorrhoids. Venereal diseases. Problems of genitalia. Miscarriage.

Moving lines

Line 1: One brings help like a mighty horse. There will be good fortune.

Fair prognosis. Alternating fever and chills. Sore throat. Chest pains. Foot pain due to cold. Constipation after diarrhea. Edema.

Line 2: One dashes to their desk. Remorse disappears.

Fair prognosis. Spleen vacuity. Liver qi rebelling up. Hysteria. Paralysis of the legs.

Line 3: One devotes oneself to a great cause. There will be no remorse.

Fair prognosis. Injury by cold wind. Viral infections. Diarrhea. Joint pains. Venereal diseases.

180

Line 4: One breaks their bond with their group. There will be supreme good fortune. People will gather together again after the dissolution, but ordinary people do not think like this.

Fair prognosis. Headaches. Dyspnea. Cold limbs.

Line 5: The imperial order is to disperse goods to people. The king thus remains without blame.

Fair prognosis. Viral infection. Weakening of the vision. Tinnitus. Boils. Venereal diseases.

Line 6: One devotes their blood to great cause and one departs to a distant place. There is no blame in this.

Fair prognosis. Cold with severe headaches. Diarrhea. Venereal diseases. Generalized pain. Depression. Ear problems. Eye diseases.

60. *Jie (Chieh)*, Limitation

There is water over the marsh,
The image of *Jie*.
Thus the superior person establishes principles
and examines the nature of virtuous behavior.

The Judgement: *Jie* means success. However, limitation cannot be persevered in if it is too rigorous.

General Indications: Chronic diseases with stagnation of damp and cold pathogenic factors. Toxic conditions. Food stagnation. Poor circulation.

Specific Indications: Joint arthritis. Phlegm stagnation. Vomiting. Diseases of oral cavity. Food stagnation. Blood stasis. Poor circulation. Constipation. Boils. Poststroke hemiplegia. Adolescent tuberculosis.

Moving lines

Line 1: If one does not go out of the garden door, one will be without blame.

Fair prognosis. Arthritis due to cold damp conditions. Toxic state. Diarrhea. Septicemia.

Line 2: If one does not go out of the garden door, one will have misfortune.

Fair prognosis. Damp heat in stomach and bladder. Acute gastritis. Cystitis. Liver qi stagnation causing subcostal spasm. Spastic pain of the legs.

Line 3: Since one knows no limitation, one will have cause to deplore. There is no blame in this.

Fair prognosis. Slow healing. Cold without fever. Boils. Leg pains due to cold. Joint pain with edema.

Line 4: One is content with one's limitations. There will be success.

Fair prognosis. Very toxic state. Severe phlegm congestion causing dyspnea.

Line 5: One gladly accepts one's limitations. There will be good fortune. Going ahead brings respect.

Fair prognosis. Extreme yin vacuity. Depression. Paralysis. Chronic indigestion.

Line 6: One suffers terribly from their limitations. Perseverance brings misfortune. Remorse disappears.

Fair prognosis. General qi vacuity. High fever. Severe headaches. Edema.

61. *Zhong Fu (Chung Fu)*, Inner Truth

Wind blows over the marsh,
The image of *Zhong Fu*.
The superior person thus reviews penalties
and delays executions.

The Judgement: *Zhong Fu* means a dolphin will bring good fortune. One should cross the great river. One should persevere.

General Indications: Yin and yang vacuity. Chronic *zang* organ diseases. Exhaustion. Heart vacuity. Possible death.

Specific Indications: Food stagnation. Viral diseases. Illnesses from liver yang repletion. Boils. Clotty menstruation.

Moving lines

Line 1: If one is faithful to their intention, one will have good fortune. If one becomes confused by others, one will not have serenity.

Fair prognosis. Latent fevers. Phlegm stagnation. Night sweats. Diarrhea. Foot pain.

Line 2: A crane is calling in the shade and its young answers it saying, "I have a fine goblet. I will share it with you."

Fair prognosis. Joint pain from liver wind. Alcohol intoxication. Breast diseases. Depression.

Line 3: One finds their foe. Now one beats the drum. Now one stops. Now one sobs. Now one sings.

184

Fair prognosis. Fever. Food stagnation. Lower back pain due to cold. Constipation. Edema. Lung vacuity. Mental confusion. Hysteria.

Line 4: The moon is nearly full. The team horse goes astray. There is no blame in this.

Fair prognosis. Stomach qi vacuity. Lack of appetite. Subcostal spasms. Pneumonia. Constipation due to heat in the large intestine. Edema. Abdominal blood stasis.

Line 5: One is sincere and united with others. There is no blame in this.

Fair prognosis. Nausea and vomiting. Summer heat stroke. Weakening of vision. Headaches. Chest and back pains.

Line 6: One is like a rooster trying to fly up to heaven. Perseverance brings misfortune.

Fair prognosis. Seasonal cold. Joint pains. Severe coughing.

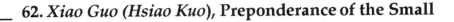

62. *Xiao Guo (Hsiao Kuo)*, Preponderance of the Small

Thunder over the mountain,
The image of *Xiao Guo*.
Thus the superior person emphasizes respect
   in conduct,
Grief in bereavement,
   and prudence in expenditure.

The Judgement: *Xiao Guo* means success through perseverance. Small things may be undertaken. But great things should not be executed. The flying bird brings a message. It is not good to fly up. It is good to stay low. There will be great good fortune.

General Indications: Interior heat and exterior cold conditions. Gastrointestinal tumors. Brain dysfunction. Kidney vacuity. General toxic state. Death.

Specific Indications: Cancer of the digestive system. Poststroke paralysis. Mental breakdown. Urogenital problems. Venereal diseases.

Moving lines

Line 1: The flying bird has misfortune.

Fair prognosis. Fever. Lack of appetite. Damp heat in the bladder. Weakening of vision.

Line 2: One passed by one's grandfather and met with their grandmother. But one never got to see the prince. They only met with his servants. There is no blame in this.

186

Fair prognosis. The illness tends to be chronic. Injury from cold. Abdominal spasms. Lower abdominal distention. Arthritis due to wind-damp.

Line 3: If one is not vigilant, one may be hit from behind. There will be misfortune.

Fair prognosis. Headaches with intermittent fever. Spleen vacuity. Liver yang repletion. Arthritis due to wind-damp.

Line 4: There is no blame for one in meeting someone without passing by. Going ahead will bring danger. One needs to be vigilant. Do not act. Persevere consistently.

Poor prognosis. Severe qi vacuity. Food poisoning. Abdominal abscess. Poststroke paralysis.

Line 5: It is very cloudy, but it has not rained in my western region. The prince shot a man in the cave.

Fair prognosis. *Jing* vacuity. Chest pain with phlegm. Problems of the throat. Depression. Venereal diseases.

Line 6: One passes by someone without meeting. The flying bird leaves one behind. There will be misfortune. This is a disaster.

Poor prognosis. Liver qi rising to the head. Headaches. Hysteria. Palpitations. Sudden death.

63. *Ji Ji (Chi Chi)*, After Completion

Water over fire,
The image of *Ji Ji*.
The superior person thus thinks of adversity
  and prevents themself from encountering it.

The Judgement: *Ji Ji* means success in small matters. One should persevere. Good fortune at the beginning, but chaos in the end.

General Indications: Yin and yang vacuity. Illnesses due to exterior cold and interior damp heat. Diseases due to excessive stress and overindulgence. An exhausted system.

Specific Indications: Heart and kidney vacuity. Exhaustion due to sexual excess. Food stagnation. Blood vacuity. Constipation. Cold and flu.

Moving lines

Line 1: One is dragging their wheels. The fox gets its tail wet. There is no blame.

Fair prognosis. Spleen and kidney vacuity. Lower back pain due to cold. Blood stasis.

Line 2: The woman lost the curtains of her carriage. Do not run after it. It will come back in seven days.

Fair prognosis. Kidney yang vacuity. Phlegm in the lungs. Edema. Constipation. Palpitations.

Line 3: Emperor Wu attacked the enemy from the West and, after three years of battle, he conquered it. Inferior people should not be employed for this.

Fair prognosis. Blood stasis. Depression. Lower back pain. Chronic lung diseases.

Line 4: The finest clothes can turn to rags. Be alert all day long.

Good prognosis. May need to change physician. Asthma due to excessive phlegm. Dyspnea. Weakening of vision.

Line 5: The eastern villager who slaughtered an ox does not gain as much blessing as the western villager who only made a small sacrifice.

Poor prognosis. Damp heat in the stomach. Boils. Generalized paralysis.

Line 6: One gets one's head wet. There may be danger.

Fair prognosis. Liver qi rising to the head. Severe headaches. Hysteria. Palpitations. Prostration.

64. *Wei Ji (Wei Chi)*, Before Completion

Fire over water,
The image of *Wei Ji*.
The superior person thus carefully examines things
in order to place them in their right place.

The Judgement: *Wei Ji* means success. The little fox got its tail wet when it almost finished crossing the stream. Nothing should be undertaken.

General Indications: Illnesses due to exterior heat and interior cold. Vacuity heat symptoms. An illness in the middle of its course.

Specific Indications: Blood stasis. Subcostal pains. Lower abdominal pain. Hysteria. Bleeding. Diarrhea. Heart and kidney vacuity.

Moving lines

Line 1: The fox gets his tail wet. There will be humiliation.

Fair prognosis. Dyspnea with phlegm. Palpitations. Blood stasis. Vomiting due to food poisoning. Foot pain due to cold. Meningitis in children.

Line 2: He brakes his wheels. Perseverance brings good fortune.

Fair prognosis. Kidney diseases. Cold with fever. Boils. Leg paralysis. Blood stasis.

Line 3: If one attacks before completion, one will meet with misfortune. One should cross the great river.

190

Fair prognosis. Severe attack of cold. Dysentery. Knee pain. Fatigue.

Line 4: Perseverance brings good fortune. Remorse disappears. The Emperor attacked the enemy from the West. After three years, he brought rewards to the great state.

Good prognosis. Diseases due to damp cold. Vision problems. Ear diseases. Boils.

Line 5: Perseverance brings good fortune. There is no remorse. The brightness of the superior person is their inner truth. There will be good fortune.

Good prognosis. Alternating fever and chills. Subcostal pain due to phlegm. Headaches. Stiff shoulder. Edema.

Line 6: One drinks wine with genuine sincerity. There is no blame in this. If one gets their head wet, they will lose their inner truth.

Good prognosis. Liver qi stagnation. Headaches. Joint pains. Fatigue. Seizures in children.

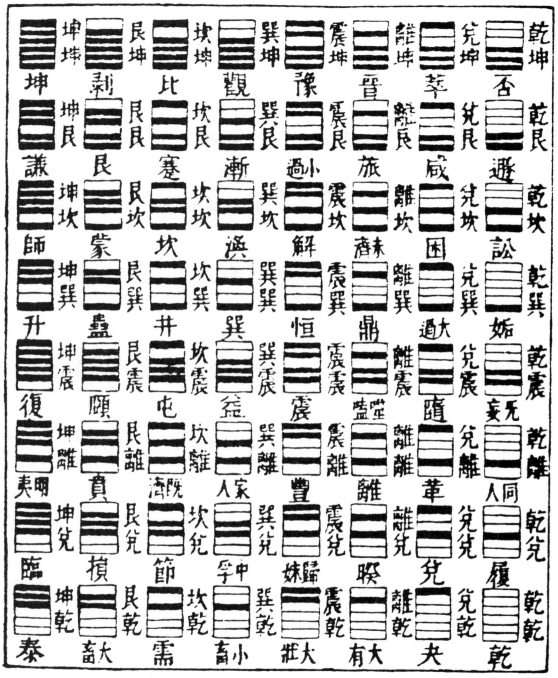

Diagram showing the yin yang proportions of the sixty-four hexagrams in terms of light and dark elements.

(From Zhang Jing-yue's *Lei Jing Tung Yi* [*The Systematic Classic's Illustrated Appendix*])

6

Classical *I Ching* Case Histories

One of the best ways to learn *I Ching* interpretation is to study as many examples of readings by past masters as possible every time one casts the *I Ching*. However, as mentioned in the introduction, due to its confidential nature, there is a scarcity in the existing *I Ching* literature on the field of medical divination which one might study. Fortunately, Daigaku Kato, one of the greatest modern Japanese *I Ching* masters, took a serious interest in medical divination and has left a small collection of medical divinations by past *I Ching* masters. He seemingly had a difficult time even gathering some sixty cases of medical readings due to their rarity in the literature. Most of these are very informative and inspirational. Due to the way they were recorded, however, being so brief and enigmatic, they are hard to read and understand, let alone translate verbatim. Most of the time, they only record which hexagrams the masters obtained and how they were interpreted, expecting the reader to figure out the rest! Therefore, instead of translating a number of these word for word, I have decided to paraphrase various examples from this collection. Hopefully these case histories will shed more light on the art of *I Ching* interpretation.[1]

Case #1

Rashu Matsui, a very famous *I Ching* scholar of the Shogunate period, was once asked to consult the *I Ching* by an elderly woman. She said that she had been healthy all her life but recently she had developed lower back pain and had

---

[1]   Kato, Daigaku, *Ekigaku Byosen (Study of Medical Divination by the I Ching)*, Kigen Shobo Publishing Company, Tokyo, 1974 (in Japanese)

not been feeling well in general. The master cast the *I Ching* and obtained the following.

Original Hexagram	New Hexagram
2	**7**
═══ ═══	═══ ═══
═══ ═══	═══ ═══
═══ ═══	═══ ═══
═══ ═══	═══════
──x──	═══ ═══
═══ ═══	═══ ═══
Kun	*Shi*
(*K'un*)	(*Shi*)

The master thought that the woman was still essentially healthy, because Hexagram 2, *Kun* (*K'un*), the Receptive, usually indicates good health in females as a whole. However, the changing second line, which converts the lower trigram *Kun* (*K'un*) to *Kan* (*K'an*), suggests stagnation of cold and toxins in the lower burner. Therefore, the master advised the woman to take an herbal tonic to warm the lower burner and to disperse these toxins. (The formula that the woman took is not recorded.) The woman took the herbs for a short period of time and became well again.[2]

This is a good case to study in detail. Master Matsui appears to have paid most of his attention to the indications of Hexagram 2 and the changing line, but there is more to be investigated. Let us examine this case a little further.

First of all, Hexagram 2, *Kun* (*K'un*), the Receptive, is the most yin hexagram out of all the 64 and represents female energy in a wholesome way. However, when there is a changing line, as in this case, it upsets the healthy integrity of the hexagram. Especially when one divides the new hexagram (Hexagram 7) into its two component trigrams, one can see what kind of forces are at work under the surface.

─────────────────

[2]   Ibid., p. 112

194

Upper Nuclear Trigram	Lower Nuclear Trigram	New Nuclear Hexagram
		24
▬▬ ▬▬ ▬▬ ▬▬ ▬▬ ▬▬	▬▬ ▬▬ ▬▬ ▬▬ ▬▬▬▬▬	▬▬ ▬▬ ▬▬ ▬▬ ▬▬ ▬▬ ▬▬ ▬▬ ▬▬ ▬▬ ▬▬▬▬▬
Kun (*K'un*)	*Zhen* (*Chen*)	*Fu* (*Fu*)

One can now see that there is recuperative power symbolized by the new nuclear Hexagram 24, *Fu* (*Fu*), Return, in this woman. Yang energy, implied by the first line, is coming back to Hexagram 2, *Kun* (*K'un*), the Receptive, to promote healing. At the same time, *Fu* (*Fu*), Return, also hints at the possible return of the same problem in the future. One can also see the lower back pain denoted by the lower nuclear trigram *Zhen* (*Chen*), the Arousing. It symbolizes acute pains which tend to come and go quickly. Thus, we can speculate that the woman not only had cold toxins (*Kan*, the Abysmal) but also had internal liver wind (*Zhen*, the Arousal), which needed to be treated as well.

Case #2

In December, 1890, Chobei Jinbo asked Donsho Takashima, the grand master of the Takashima School, to cast the *I Ching* on his wife's prognosis. She had been suffering from gastric cancer. Upon consultation, the master obtained the following.

Original Hexagram	New Hexagram
5	9
———x———	———————
———————	———————
——— ———	——— ———
———————	———————
———————	———————
———————	———————
Xu	*Xiao Xu*
(Hsu)	*(Hsiao Ch'u)*

The master interpreted the oracle to mean that she would have some time left to live (*Xu*, Waiting), even though she was bound to pass away from the illness. He told Mr. Jinbo that, since Hexagram 5 is one of the *you hun* (Wandering Spirit) hexagrams, her prognosis was extremely poor. At the same time, the text for the top line of this hexagram reads,

> One has fallen into the pit.
> Three uninvited guests have arrived.
> Honoring them brings good fortune in the end.

The master said that this was also ominous, for the pit symbolizes burial, the three uninvited guests imply priests for a funeral, and "honoring them brings good fortune in the end" denotes death. It turned out that, several days later, as the master had predicted, the wife passed away peacefully.[3]

There are two important things that this record does not mention about this reading. One is about the top line of Hexagram 5, *Xu (Hsu)*, Waiting, and the other is the symbolism of Hexagram 9, *Xiao Xu (Hsiao Ch'u)*, the Taming Power

---

[3]   Ibid., 122
The Takashima School of *Yi Jing* Divination is the largest organization of professional *Yi Jing* practitioners in Japan. In this particular school, the greatest emphasis is placed on symbolic association of the exact language of the *Yi Jing* text itself, rather than resorting to systematic analysis of trigrams, hexagrams, and lines.

of the Small. Although it was rather clear that the wife was dying from the facts mentioned above, one can also stipulate that she was in the terminal stage of her illness from the fact that the top line was changing. It is often observed by many masters of medical divination that a changing at the top tends to denote the terminal stage of an illness.

However, Hexagram 9, *Xiao Xu* (*Hsiao Ch'u*) also suggests that the wife still had some time left before her impending death, because the fundamental characteristic of this hexagram is "small accumulation" denoting she still had some qi left to go on for a while. In a sense, the *I Ching's* answer was redundant. This phenomenon of redundancy is quite common in the way the *I Ching* answers questions. It is like an old wise man giving the same advice in several different ways until one gets the point of what he is saying.

Case #3

Master Yuken Nishio was asked to consult the *I Ching* by one of his friends concerning the prognosis of his elderly parent. (The record does not specify the sex of the parent.) Upon consultation, he obtained the following.

Original Hexagram	New Hexagram
8	20
——x——	————
—— ——	—— ——
—— ——	—— ——
—— ——	—— ——
—— ——	—— ——
————	—— ——
Bi	*Guan*
(*Pi*)	(*Kuan*)

The master told the friend that the lower trigram, *Kun* (*K'un*) symbolizes the spleen and stomach and the upper trigram *Kan* (*Kan*) denotes stagnation of toxic food. The changed hexagram also suggests great stagnation of the whole system causing collapse. Therefore the prognosis was very poor. Later, the friend reported to Master Nishio that the person had expired from extreme emaciation due to inability to eat.[4]

In this particular case, besides what the record says, we can also see that the whole hexagram *Bi* signifies stagnation to begin with. We can also observe that the top changing line signifies the terminal stage of the person's illness. And, if we study *Bi*'s nuclear hexagram, we can even see the forces working under the surface in this particular patient.

Original Hexagram	**Nuclear Hexagram**
8	23
▬▬▬▬▬	▬▬▬▬▬
▬▬ ▬▬	▬▬ ▬▬
▬▬ ▬▬	▬▬ ▬▬
▬▬ ▬▬	▬▬ ▬▬
▬▬ ▬▬	▬▬ ▬▬
▬▬ ▬▬	▬▬▬▬▬
Bi	*Bo*
(*Pi*)	(*Po*)

As one can see, nuclear Hexagram 23, *Bo* (*Po*), Splitting Apart, demonstrates that the patient was truly depleted of vital energy. The text for the general indications for this hexagram says, "General degeneration, deficiency of qi and blood, yin and yang exhaustion, etc." Thus we can clearly see that the patient not only had stagnation but was also severely depleted of qi and blood. Therefore, the problem was profound and death was imminent.

Case #4

In the fall of 1933, Master Daigaku Kato was asked by his sister to consult the *I Ching* about her eye condition. He cast it on diagnosis and obtained

---

[4]   Ibid., p. 133

Hexagram 13, *Tong Ren (T'ung Jen)*, Fellowship with People, with the changing fifth line, resulting in Hexagram 30, *Li (Li)*, the Clinging, Fire.

Original Hexagram	New Hexagram
13	30

Tong Ren
(T'ung Jen)

Li
(Li)

The master told her that, since Hexagram 13, *Tong Ren*, Fellowship with People, symbolizes contagious diseases, her eye problem must be an infection. He also told her that the infection was of a virulent nature because the new hexagram, *Li*, denotes an aggressive hot condition. As far as the prognosis was concerned, he told her that it was good and that only the right eye would be affected, but not the left eye, because the upper trigram (*Qian*, the Creative) of the original hexagram with the changing line symbolizes the right side of the body. The woman went to an ophthalmologist and, exactly as the *I Ching* had suggested, the infection got better fast and her left eye was left intact.[5]

In the *I Ching*, yang denotes the right side of the body and yin signifies the left. For example, the judgement for line 2 of Hexagram 36, *Ming Yi (Ming I)*, Darkening of the Light, says,

> Darkening of the light injures one in the left thigh.
> Helping the one with a powerful horse brings great fortune.

And the judgement for line 4 of the same hexagram states,

---

[5]   Ibid., p. 150

One pierces the left side of their abdomen
To get at the heart of the dark light.
They go out from the gate of the courtyard.

These judgements mention the left side of the body because, in this particular hexagram, changing lines 2 and 4 are yin lines. On the contrary, the judgement for line 3 of Hexagram 55, *Feng (Feng)*, Abundance, states,

The curtains are so thick
That small stars can be seen at noon.
One breaks their right arm.
There is no fault in this.

This judgement mentions the right arm because the third line of this hexagram is a yang line. Thus, when one needs to determine the laterality of the body, one should look at the changing line and see whether it is yang or yin.

Case #5

Kokusui Tanaka, a student of Master Bendo Shaku, was asked by a farmer to consult the *I Ching* about the condition of his sick cow. After casting, Tanaka obtained Hexagram 15, *Qian (Ch'ien)*, Modesty, with the fifth line changing, resulting in Hexagram 39, *Jian (Chien)*, Obstruction.

Original Hexagram	New Hexagram
15	39

Qian	Jian
(Ch'ien)	(Chien)

Tanaka told the farmer that the cow was exhausted by hard labor because *Qian* (*Ch'ien*), Modesty, generally implies fatigue of the whole body. Especially since the changed hexagram, *Jian* (*Chien*), Obstruction, usually suggests paralysis, he also told the farmer that the cow might be suffering insensibility of her legs due to stagnation of blood and cold. Based on suggestions from Tanaka, the cow was subsequently treated by blood-letting and acupuncture and was soon brought back to good health.[6]

There are a few further observations which might be added to Tanaka's interpretation. First of all, let's look at *Qian*'s nuclear hexagram.

	Original Hexagram		**Nuclear Hexagram**
	15		40

| | *Qian* (*Ch'ien*) | | *Jie* (*Hsieh*) |

By looking at the nuclear hexagram embodied within the original hexagram, one can see the mechanism rsponsible for the cow's symptomatology. This is evident from the nuclear hexagram *Jie* (*Hsieh*), Deliverance, which denotes internal toxins moving toward the exterior surface, and disharmony of the qi and blood. The animal was not only fatigued and paralyzed by heavy labor but also was toxic from imbalance of qi and blood. At the same time, as far as treatment is concerned, Hexagram 40, Deliverance, clearly suggests detoxification of the system by discharging toxins from the body. The method of detoxification could be blood-letting, application of cleansing herbs, or acupuncture treatment. Thus, analysis of a nuclear hexagram also suggests

---

[6]   Ibid., p. 156

various ways of treating one's patients' conditions, and it is extremely important to go through this process if one is to help one's patients not only symptomatically but also etiologically.

As far as the changing line in the fifth position is concerned, we may also speculate that the animal may have needed surgery, and it may have also suffered from damp heat in the chest and spleen.

Case #6

One day in March 1934, Dr. Jukaku Tashiro, a serious student of the *I Ching* under Master Kato's guidance, received a call from his fellow physician referring a patient to his hospital for consultation. Being very curious, before actually seeing the patient, Dr. Tashiro consulted the *I Ching* and obtained the following.

16

Yu
(*Yu*)

Dr. Tashiro speculated that the patient had serious liver qi stagnation (the upper trigram *Zhen*, the Arousing), conquering the spleen and the stomach (the lower trigram *Kun*, the Receptive) causing deep pains in their abdomen. In addition, he stipulated that the patient also suffered from severe food stagnation (the only yang line at the fourth position) and from pains from epigastric spasms (the master line of the hexagram on the fifth position).

It turned out that, when he saw the patient the next day, he exhibited exactly the same symptomatology as the doctor had already learned from his *I Ching* consultation.[7]

As Dr. Tashiro had surmised, the trigram *Zhen* (*Chen*), the Arousing, symbolizes liver yang, pathogenic wind, pains, etc. Since it is on top of the trigram *Kun* (*K'un*), the Receptive, denoting the digestive system, he analyzed the whole hexagram to mean that the liver was causing problems to the spleen and stomach. If the situation had been reversed, he might have interpreted this as denoting a preponderance of spleen repletion in the patient's condition.

He also paid special attention to the only yang line in the fourth position, which corresponds to the upper abdomen, and he was observant enough to speculate that there was a yang quality change happening in the stomach. Since there was no changing line, the patient's condition must be chronic and stationary.

As far as the master line of a hexagram is concerned in medical divination, there are various opinions among scholars. Some pay attention to this line and others fail to mention anything about it. Traditionally, there are two different types of master line in the *I Ching*. One is called a composing master line and the other is called a governing master line. Composing lines are those that give the hexagram its representative characteristics as a hexagram, regardless of the virtue or goodness of its position. The top yin line of Hexagram 43, *Guai* (*Kuai*), Breakthrough, is a good example.

43

Guai
(*Kuai*)

---

[7]   Ibid., p. 159

The top line is the only yin line which is, therefore, the only weak element in this particular hexagram. There is no virtue or goodness in this broken line's being in that position. However, since this yin line gives the idea of breakthrough to the entire hexagram, it is called the composing master line. On the contrary, a governing master line always has goodness and virtue in a proper position. It is usually the fifth line of the hexagram, but it occasionally can be some other line.[8]

Case #7

A student of Master Manase was asked by a pregnant woman to consult the *I Ching* on her condition. She stated that she had been suffering from edema of her feet and had tried many kinds of therapy, including laxative herbs, without any improvement. Upon consultation, the student obtained the following.

Original Hexagram	New Hexagram
19	24

Lin   *Fu*
(*Lin*)   (*Fu*)

The student told the woman that the laxative herbs that her doctor prescribed had removed too much yang qi and had exacerbated her condition (the second

---

[8]   I have not otherwise discussed the master lines in this book for fear it would be too confusing for many people to include this aspect of the *I Ching* into interpreting each hexagram. Instead, I have included the medical readings for the master lines in each hexagram directly into the indications of each hexagram so that the reader does not have to bother looking up master lines for each hexagram every time they cast the *I Ching*.

line changing to yin). He told the woman she should take a formula that would eliminate liver qi stagnation (the lower trigram, *Zhen*, the Arousing) which was suppressing the function of the spleen. Based on this advice, the woman took a formula to eliminate liver qi stagnation and the edema was completely eradicated (Hexagram 24, *Fu*, Return).[9]

In this particular case, one can observe an interesting occurrence when one looks at the nuclear hexagram.

Original Hexagram	Nuclear Hexagram
19	24

Lin	Fu
(*Lin*)	(*Fu*)

It turns out that the nuclear hexagram and the changed hexagram are both Hexagram 24, *Fu*, Return. This denotes the etiology of the woman's problem in a repetitive manner! This kind of situation does not happen very often, but, when it does, the *I Ching* is strongly expressing its opinion about the patient's condition and one should listen to it very carefully.

Case #8

Master Rashu Matsui was once asked by Mr. Okawa about his father's condition. Mr. Okawa told the master that the elderly man was a drinker and that, every night when he was about to go to sleep, he would suffer terribly

---

9   Kato, op.cit., p. 169

from severe spasms of his neck and shoulder, extending to his elbows. Upon consultation, the master obtained the following.

Original Hexagram	New Hexagram
53	20

Jian
(*Chien*)

Guan
(*Kuan*)

The master told Mr. Okawa that the toxins from sake (*Kan*, the Abysmal of the lower nuclear trigram) had stagnated in the middle of the stomach (*Kun*, the Receptive, of the lower nuclear trigram of *Jian*). The master told him that it was, therefore, imperative for his father to quit drinking completely and to take an herbal formula to detoxify the poisons from the sake. Mr. Okawa later told Master Matsui that his father's complaints were entirely eradicated after he did exactly as the master had suggested.[10]

In this particular case, the master appears to have paid most of his attention to the lower nuclear trigram because that is where the changes were happening. Let us look at the nuclear trigrams in detail.

---

[10] Ibid., p. 172

Regrettably, in many cases like this, *I Ching* masters did not record the content of herbal formulas because often they were not herbalists themselves.

Original Hexagram	Upper Nuclear Trigram	Lower Nuclear Trigram	New Hexagram
53			64
Jian (Chien)	Li (Li)	Kan (K'an)	Wei Ji (Wei Chi)

First of all, the upper nuclear trigram, *Li*, the Clinging or Fire, symbolizes a hot condition in the upper body because it is the upper nuclear trigram. With *Kan*, the Abysmal or Water, underneath, it gives us the picture of toxins from alcohol in the stomach giving rise to a hot condition in the neck and shoulder region, which is where the man had his complaints. Therefore, first of all, it was absolutely necessary for the man to get rid of the toxins, and, at the same time, to take herbs to disperse the heat in the upper burner. However, when one looks at the new nuclear hexagram, one can clearly see that, even though his complaints were controlled, he was not completely well. This is because *Wei Ji*, Before Completion, strongly suggests that the man would have a condition of exterior heat and interior cold. Therefore, his physician should have given him an herbal formula to correct this condition after detoxifying the alcohol.

Case #9

In the fall of 1932, Master Daigaku Kato was asked to consult the oracle by his friend about the prognosis of a construction worker who fell one day from a building at Moriyama Park in Setagaya district in Tokyo. Upon casting, the master acquired the following.

Original Hexagram	New Hexagram
22	36

Bi	*Ming Yi*
(*Pi*)	(*Ming I*)

The master told his friend that the man's prognosis was very grave since *Bi*, Grace, changing to *Ming Yi*, Darkening of the Light, was an extremely ominous omen. At the same time, since the changing line at the sixth position suggested a terminal state, the master told the inquirer that the man's death was imminent. It turned out that the injured man passed away the day after the accident, as the *I Ching* master had predicted.[11]

First of all, even though Kato does not mention this in his record, the upper trigram, *Gen* (*Ken*), Keeping Still or Mountain, means trauma in general. Especially, the changing line at the top strongly suggests possible head trauma in this case. Based on the history of the patient, this is not a far-fetched probability. Therefore, the changing line at the sixth position suggests not only a terminal condition but also a head injury being the cause of the swift death. In addition, when one analyzes the nuclear trigrams and nuclear hexagrams of *Bi*, Grace, one can see yet another message of death from the *I Ching* in this case.

---

[11]   Ibid., p. 179

Original Hexagram	Upper Nuclear Trigram	Lower Nuclear Trigram	New Nuclear Hexagram
22			40
Bi (Pi)	Zhen (Chen)	Kan (K'an)	Jie (Hsieh)

The upper nuclear trigram, *Zhen*, the Arousing, Thunder, denotes shock and pains from trauma, and *Kan*, the Abysmal or Water, symbolizes bleeding from the injury. The new nuclear hexagram, *Jie*, Deliverance, suggests liberation from the physical existence in the sense that some Buddhists call death the great liberation. In this short analysis, one can easily see that there are abundant indications of the poor man's predicament in both the nuclear trigrams and hexagram. Therefore, it is imperative to deeply investigate the nature of a hexagram by analyzing its nuclear trigrams and hexagram.

Case #10

One day in the spring of 1882, Master Donsho Takashima was asked by Mr. Jotaro Mori, secretary of a trading firm called America Ichiban, to consult the *I Ching* about his condition. Mr. Mori told the master that he had started having intermittent pains in his abdomen and had consulted doctors of internal medicine and surgery but that they had not helped him at all. In the mean time, the pains had become so exacerbated that he could no longer eat. Upon casting, Master Takashima obtained the following.

Original Hexagram	New Hexagram
23	20

Bo
(*Po*)   *Guan*
(*Kuan*)

The master told Mr. Mori that *Bo*, Splitting Apart, was not a very auspicious hexagram in general because it usually means collapse of yin and yang. However, since the changing line was at the fifth position, he said that Mr. Mori might have some time before he might run into a serious situation. The master told him that, since the judgement for the fifth line said,

> Speared fish.
> Support will come from the courtesans.
> There is nothing that cannot improve.

he suggested trying acupuncture treatment ("Speared fish"). To the great surprise of Mr. Mori, he happened to know an acupuncturist called Mr. Wakamiya, which literally means "young courtesans", and he, therefore, went to him for treatment which, as it turned out, cured his abdominal problem in a short period of time!

After the *I Ching* master learned what had happened to Mr. Mori, he wrote,

> I am not a professional medical man. Especially, when it comes to acupuncture, I don't even know what it's good for. However, because of what the *I Ching* symbolism suggested, I decided to recommend acupuncture treatment. Now, I have heard of the miraculous results, and I am convinced that acupuncture can perform great cure of diseases depending on what the illness is. At the same time, I am

utterly awe-stricken to know that the subtle principles of the *I Ching* can be so precise to such degree of detail in divination![12]

Case #11

One student studying under Master Hakuga Arai, a very prominent *I Ching* scholar during the Shogunate period, was asked to consult the *I Ching* by a pregnant woman about the outlook of her imminent delivery. Upon consultation, the student obtained Hexagram 24, *Fu* (*Fu*), Return, changing to Hexagram 51, *Zhen* (*Chen*), the Arousing.

Original Hexagram	New Hexagram
24	51
———— ————	———— ————
————x————	———— ————
———— ————	———— ————
———— ————	———— ————
Fu	*Zhen*
(*Fu*)	(*Chen*)

Before telling the woman the results of the consultation, the student conferred with Master Arai. He told the master that, in his opinion, the delivery would be difficult because the new hexagram, *Zhen* (*Chen*), the Arousing, denotes various kinds of distress. The master disagreed with the student and said that the delivery would be uneventful and the baby would be a boy. He explained to the student that the hexagram *Fu*, Return, comes about by a yang line entering Hexagram 2, *Kun* (*K'un*), the Receptive, which symbolizes healthy pregnancy. In addition, the new hexagram, *Zhen*, the Arousing, denotes the first son and heightened activity or a quick delivery.

---

[12]   Ibid., p. 182

It turned out that the woman delivered a healthy baby boy after a short labor the day after the consultation.[13]

Case #12

Master Chushu Manase was asked to cast the *I Ching* by a woman who said that she had not had her period for seven months and that she had no appetite at all. She also told the master that when she took the medicine prescribed by her doctor, it caused her chest to hurt. She asked the master to ascertain the etiology and treatment plan for her. Upon consultation, the master obtained Hexagram 32, *Heng* (Heng), Duration, changing to Hexagram 40, *Jie* (Hsieh), Deliverance.

Original Hexagram	New Hexagram
32	40
———— ———— ———— ———— ————o———— ———— ———— ———— ———— ———— ————	———— ———— ———— ———— ———— ———— ———— ———— ———— ———— ———— ————
Heng (Heng)	*Jie* (Hsieh)

The master told the woman that the root of her problem was stagnation of liver qi, which was represented by *Sun*, the Gentle, Wind, and *Zhen* (the Arousing, Thunder) in Hexagram 32 and another *Zhen* (the Arousing, Thunder) in the new hexagram. He said that excessive liver wind was causing heart fire (*Li*, the Clinging, Fire as the lower nuclear trigram). The master also told the woman that she had excessive stagnation of fluid and blood (*Kan*, the Abysmal, Water) in the middle and lower burners, represented in the upper and lower nuclear trigrams in Hexagram 32 and the upper nuclear trigram and the lower trigram

---

13   Ibid., p. 186

of Hexagram 40. Therefore, the master said that it was essential for her not only to remove liver wind and calm down heart fire, but also to expel the water and blood stagnation in her abdomen. With this information, the woman went back to her doctor and obtained a new herbal formula which brought her back to good health very quickly.[14]

In this case, the *I Ching* demonstrated excessive liver wind and severe stagnation of water and blood in three places, as seen above. When the *I Ching* repeats its symbolic expressions of pathogenesis, the physician should attend the problems at the same time immediately, instead of treating them separately. In other words, the woman needed to be helped with the liver wind problem and with the water and blood stagnation at once. Otherwise, one thing would cause the other to create more diseased conditions in a successive manner.

Case #13

Master Kakushu Inouye was asked to cast the *I Ching* on the diagnosis and prognosis of a young sick boy by his father. Upon consulting, he obtained Hexagram 35, *Jin (Chin)*, Progress, changing to Hexagram 12, *Pi (P'i)*, Standstill.

Original Hexagram	New Hexagram
35	12
Jin (*Chin*)	*Pi* (*P'i*)

---

[14]   Ibid., p. 211

The master told the father that *Jin*, Progress, denoted a progressive, contagious disease. Its upper trigram, *Li* (the Clinging, Fire), symbolizes heat in the eyes. Especially when it changes to *Qian* (The Creative, Heaven), it is usually serious, and could mean swelling of the eyes with heat. The lower trigram, *Kun* (*K'un*), the Receptive, Earth, denotes the skin. Therefore, the whole hexagram symbolizes progressive, contagious illness of the eyes and the skin, probably smallpox, which later on was confirmed to be the case. The master also said to the man that, as far as prognosis was concerned, the disease would come to a standstill (the new hexagram *Pi*), but his eyes would not be healed. It turned out that the boy did not die from smallpox, but went blind as the master had predicted.[15]

Case #14

Master Chushu Manase was inquired by a patient about his condition and prognosis. Upon consultation, the master acquired Hexagram 36, *Ming Yi* (*Ming I*), Darkening of the Light, changing to Hexagram 11, *Tai* (*T'ai*), Peace.

Original Hexagram	New Hexagram
36	11

Ming Yi	*Tai*
(*Ming I*)	(*T'ai*)

The master told the patient that he had pathogenic heat in his lower body (the lower trigram, *Li*, the Clinging, Fire) which was causing him pains (the lower nuclear trigram, *Kan*, the Abysmal, Water) in the lower abdomen (the second

---

15   Ibid., p. 220

changing line and upper trigram *Kun*, the Receptive, Earth). However, the master said that, if the heat (*Li*, the lower trigram) were cooled to change to *Qian* (*Ch'ien*) like in the new trigram, *Tai*, Peace, the patient would be brought back to good health. Based on this advice, the patient took medicine to expel heat and was soon restored to health.[16]

Case #15

Master Chushu Manase consulted the *I Ching* on a patient who had been ill for a long time and obtained Hexagram 44, *Gou* (*Kou*), Coming to Meet, changing to Hexagram 57, *Sun* (*Sun*), the Gentle.

Original Hexagram	New Hexagram
44	57

Gou
(*Kou*)

Sun
(*Sun*)

The master said to the patient that the hexagram *Gou* (*Kou*), Coming to Meet, usually symbolizes an unimportant contagious illness like the flu. However, the original illness was not treated properly, and it created heat in the middle burner (*Li*, Fire in the upper nuclear trigram in Hexagram 57) and that this had caused severe internal liver wind to rise (the four *Sun*, Wind, trigrams in Hexagrams 44 and 57). With this information, the patient went to another physician and obtained a new prescription to correct the heat and liver wind. The master was later told that the patient had been restored to normal condition.[17]

---

[16]   Iibd., p. 223

[17]   Ibid., p. 247

Case #16

Master Ryuzan Tanigawa cast the *I Ching* for a patient and obtained Hexagram 45, *Cui (Ts'ui)*, Gathering Together, changing to Hexagram 31, *Xian (Hsien)*, Influence.

Original Hexagram	New Hexagram
45	31

Cui
(Ts'ui)

Xian
(Hsien)

The master said to the man that *Cui*, Gathering Together, with the third line changing, symbolized toxic food stagnation due to chronic spleen and stomach vacuity. However, if he could correct the condition by proper treatment, his prognosis was good, which was denoted by *Xian*, Influence. The patient followed the master's advice for a while and improved quite a bit. However, as soon as he started feeling better, he went back to his old bad habits. When the patient came back for another consultation, the master obtained Hexagram 31, *Xian (Hsien)*, Influence, changing to Hexagram 45, *Cui (Ts'ui)*, Gathering Together.

Original Hexagram	New Hexagram
31	45

Xian
(Hsien)

Cui
(Ts'ui)

The master told the man that his prognosis was rather poor because he was full of toxins (*Cui*, Gathering Together) and had exhausted his qi and blood. Later on, the master was told that the patient had passed away as he had prognosticated.[18]

This example was not clearly recorded and it needs some explication. First of all, since the original Hexagram 31, *Xian*, Influence, usually denotes infectious illnesses, we can stipulate that the man had an infection in the abdomen, which is indicated by the third changing line of the original hexagram. Further, if one divides the hexagram *Xian*, Influence into its component nuclear trigrams, one can see an even deeper etiology.

Upper Nuclear Trigram	Lower Nuclear Trigram	Nuclear Hexagram 44
Qian (Ch'ien)	Sun (Sun)	Gou (Kou)

The upper nuclear trigram *Qian* (*Ch'ien*), The Creative, Heaven, usually denotes severe yang conditions and the lower nuclear trigram *Sun* (*Sun*) symbolizes wind illnesses coming from liver malfunction. The nuclear hexagram *Gou*, Coming to Meet, usually signifies yin vacuity and false yang repletion. Therefore, we can conjecture that the man may have had liver yin vacuity and false yang repletion causing wind conditions which oppressed the functions of the stomach, thus causing severe toxic conditions in the organ. We may even stipulate that the man had stomach cancer which metastasized to the liver.

---

[18]   Ibid., p. 250

Unfortunately, there is no way left for us to confirm this speculation, but we can certainly gain deep insight by analyzing the nuclear trigrams in otherwise obscure cases like this.

Case #17

In July of 1887, *I Ching* master Donsho Takashima was staying at an inn at Hakone Hot Springs in order to avoid a cholera epidemic which happened to be spreading quickly in Tokyo at that time. Mr. Fujita, an antique dealer from Tokyo who was also staying at the hotel, asked Master Takashima to cast the *I Ching* on one of his relatives because he had just received a telegram notifying that the woman was stricken with cholera. Upon consultation, the master obtained Hexagram 47, *Kun* (*K'un*), Oppression, changing to Hexagram 28, *Da Guo* (*Ta Kuo*), Preponderance of the Great.

Original Hexagram	New Hexagram
47	28
Kun (*K'un*)	*Da Guo* (*Ta Kuo*)

The master said the prognosis for the woman was rather bleak because the *Xi Ci Chuan* (*Commentary on Appended Judgement*) on the third line of Hexagram 47, *Kun* (*K'un*), Oppression reads:

> One is hurt by stone
> And is leaning on thorns and thistles.
> Even though he enters his house,
> He does not see his wife.
> There will be misfortune.

In addition, since the new hexagram, *Da Guo* (*Ta Kuo*), Preponderance of the Great, symbolizes a coffin, the master told Mr. Fujita that the death of the woman was imminent. It turned out that the next day Mr. Fujita received a telegram from Tokyo informing him of the woman's death. The mysterious thing was that the time when the master cast the *I Ching* coincided with the moment of the woman's death![19]

Although the record indicates that the master placed great emphasis on the annotation and the changed hexagram to come up with his judgement, this casting is awash with clinical information about the patient's condition. First of all, *Kun* (*K'un*), Oppression, is a hexagram which denotes vacuity of yin and yang, inability to recover from an illness, emaciation, etc., and this hexagram alone shows serious adversity. On top of that, the upper trigram, *Dui* (*Tui*), the Joyous, Lake, is a symbol of the mouth and digestive tract and denotes diseases obtained through the oral tract which is the case with cholera. It also is a symbol of accumulation of poisons and toxins.

In addition, the lower trigram is *Kan* (*K'an*), The Abysmal, Water, which again symbolizes toxins and blood in the lower part of the body. Especially with the changing line at the third level transforming the *Kan* trigram into *Sun*, the Gentle, Wind, these toxins would be spread like wind in storm. In an extremely virulent disease like cholera, a *Kan* trigram changing to *Sun* is a very fitting symbolism for the situations of this woman.

Secondly, when one divides the new hexagram, *Da Guo* (*Ta Kuo*), Preponderance of the Great, into its component nuclear trigrams, one finds more messages from the *I Ching* about this patient.

---

[19]   Ibid., p. 256
As stated previously, *I Ching* Masters of the Takashima School tend to place great emphasis on the exact words of the annotation on each hexagram and its changing lines. However, it is not common that one can find an appropriate judgement from the *I Ching* in such exact words in a literal sense as this case. Usually, figurative interpretation is required to extract a message from the *I Ching*.

Upper Nuclear	Lower Nuclear	New Hexagram
═══════ ═══════ ═══════	═══════ ═══════ ═══════	═══════ ═══════ ═══════ ═══════
Qian (*Ch'ien*)	*Qian* (*Ch'ien*)	*Qian* (*Ch'ien*)

As one sees here, all the nuclear trigrams are *Qian* (*Ch'ien*), the Creative, Heaven, denoting an extremely violent and powerful disease. The nuclear hexagram is also *Qian*, again symbolizing the most yang and aggressive conditions. In this sense, *Qian* is the most grave omen obtained in the case of any serious illness.

Case #18

In May of 1934, Master Yinsei Morizawa was asked to cast the *I Ching* by a woman about her son's condition; he was a student at Hokkaido University. She said that her son had just sent her a letter and had claimed that he had been diagnosed by his doctor with beriberi, for which the physician had recommended hydrotherapy. Upon consultation, the master obtained Hexagram 51, *Zhen* (*Chen*), the Arousing, Thunder, changing to Hexagram 16, *Yu* (*Yu*), Enthusiasm.

Original Hexagram	New Hexagram
51	16
Zhen (*Chen*)	*Yu* (*Yu*)

220

The master said to the woman that he thought her son was not telling the truth about his illness because the commentary on the bottom line of Hexagram *Zhen* (*Chen*), the Arousing, states:

> First thunder comes with Oh, oh!,
> Then laughing comes with Ha, ha!.
> There will be good fortune.

The master said that this was an auspicious indication to begin with and, in addition, the new hexagram, *Yu* (*Yu*), Enthusiasm, was also a sign of happiness and normalcy for a young student. Therefore, Morizawa told the mother that her son was just pretending to be sick to obtain some free time and additional funds from her to dally around. Although the woman was not really happy about the reading, she did go visit her son in Sapporo City, and it turned out that the young fellow was in quite good health and was idling very much at school![20]

Case #19

Master Zuitei Hirazawa was asked to cast the *I Ching* on a young girl who had become acutely sick. Upon consultation, the master obtained Hexagram 54, *Gui Mei* (*Kuei Mei*), the Marrying Maiden, changing to Hexagram 38, *Kui* (*K'uei*), Opposition.

---

[20]   Ibid., p. 268
       One tends to obtain this kind of reading about patients who tend to be psychosomatic, hypochondriacs, or histrionic. When the patient's complaints are very different from what one obtains from their *I Ching* consultation, one should look into the patient's case more deeply than usual, because there are things about which the patient is not telling the truth. Also, when one obtains Hexagram 4, *Meng* (*Mêng*), Youthful Folly, the *Yi Jing* is often giving one the message that they are being fooled by their patient or by their own ignorance or prejudice.

Original Hexagram	New Hexagram
54	38

Gui Mei	*Kui*
(*Kuei Mei*)	(*K'uei*)

The master said that *Gui Mei* with the first line changing suggests that the girl had been suffering from a *shang han* syndrome (damage due to cold) with high fever, headache, palpitations, constipation, and anuria(See Chapter 5). He also said that there must be two sick people in the family as represented by the upper trigram, *Zhen* (*Chen*), the Arousing, Thunder, for the first son, and by the lower trigram, *Dui* (*Tui*), the Joyous, Lake, for the third daughter. The man who had asked for the consultation said that the master was correct. Master Hirazawa went on to say that the oldest son had a poor prognosis because the heat (the upper trigram, *Li*, the Clinging, Fire) would consume him, but, as far as the daughter was concerned, she would slowly recover because *Dui* symbolizes slow recovery and there was no changing line in it. It turned out that the eldest son passed away in spite of intense care, but the girl was saved as the master had predicted.[21]

In some traditional schools of *I Ching* interpretation, trigrams may be seen as representing multiple persons or entities. In this case, the trigrams were interpreted in the context of family members according to the correspondences outlined in Chapter 2. They could also be seen in the context of an organization such as a government, corporation, school, etc.

---

[21]   Ibid., p. 276

What might the reading be in this case if one were to interpret the original hexagram entirely in terms of the girl? First of all, the text for the sixth line of Hexagram 54, *Gui Mei* (*Kuei Mei*), the Marrying Maiden, reads, "Fair prognosis. High fever. Headaches. Palpitations. Heat blisters in the mouth. Constipation." Therefore, without considering the eldest son's situation, one can still see the symptoms and the prognosis for the young girl. As far as the outcome of the *shang han* syndrome is concerned, we can speculate that she must have had a hard time recovering because Hexagram 38, *Kui* (*K'uei*), Opposition, denotes accumulation of hot toxins in the body.

Case #20

Master Chushu Manase was asked to cast the *I Ching* on the condition of a patient who was suffering from hypertension. Upon consultation, the master obtained Hexagram 62, *Xiao Guo* (*Hsiao Kuo*), Preponderance of the Small, changing to Hexagram 16, *Yu* (*Yu*), Enthusiasm.

Original Hexagram	New Hexagram
62	16
▬▬▬ ▬▬▬	▬▬▬ ▬▬▬
▬▬▬ ▬▬▬	▬▬▬ ▬▬▬
▬▬▬o▬▬▬	▬▬▬ ▬▬▬
▬▬▬ ▬▬▬	▬▬▬ ▬▬▬
▬▬▬ ▬▬▬	▬▬▬ ▬▬▬
Xiao Guo (*Hsiao Kuo*)	*Yu* (*Yu*)

Master Manase told the patient that he had a great amount of heat in the middle burner (the two yang lines) from excessive consumption of meat. The master told the man that the heat was stagnating the qi and blood (the upper nuclear trigram *Dui*, the Joyous, Lake), and that that would eventually cause a stroke (the new hexagram *Yu*). The master suggested he should correct his

223

life style. Master Manase later learned that the patient did pass away from cerebral hemorrhage because the man did not take his advice seriously.[22]

[22]   Ibid., p. 300

Epilogue

What I have attempted to offer in this book is a concise yet systematic overview of the applications of the *I Ching* in medical practice. There is a great deal more that could be said on this subject, but this is a good place to start. As one practices it, one will find new symbolic messages of one's own every day, and their understanding of this book will become richer and deeper. This is such an inspiring and exciting process!

If one has been practicing rational and theoretical systems of medicine, it may be an adventure to become involved with the *I Ching*. One may at first feel skeptical and resistent. However, there are many ways to know things. Logical and rational modalities are not the only way to understand the world. Intuition is another way to know the universe. The *I Ching*'s way of approaching the vast knowledge to which each of us has access is alinear and synchronic. Since most of us are so used to thinking in scientific, inductive, and reductionistic ways, intuitive cognition or direct perception of the world has been pushed aside as something primitive and unproven.

However, modern physicists are now telling us that the universe is not really a place of consistent natural laws but a place of great disorder, a chaos with constant changes. They claim that there is absolutely nothing completely predictable in the universe. Even the motion of an electron is not completely predictable! They can only find some "patterns" in the great chaos of energy fields.

This understanding of the universe is exactly the same as that of the *I Ching*. The universe is constantly changing in extremely unpredictable ways with some recognizable patterns. This is also so in the practice of medicine. Although we have learned numerous laws and principles, we can never predict anything with complete certitude. We can only observe a certain number of patterns, and we must admit that, in spite of great technological advancement, medicine is still largely a mystery. However, when facing this mystery, we as practitioners can obtain a great deal of assistance from the *I Ching*. Intuitive knowledge has profound power. Let this power be your guide in medical practice.

Chart for Identifying Hexagram Numbers

Upper Trigram ⇒ / Lower Trigram ⇓	1	4	6	7	8	5	3	2
1	1	34	5	26	11	9	14	43
4	25	51	3	27	24	42	21	17
6	6	40	29	4	7	59	64	47
7	33	62	39	52	15	53	56	31
8	12	16	8	23	2	20	35	45
5	44	32	48	18	46	57	50	28
3	13	55	63	22	36	37	30	49
2	10	54	60	41	19	61	38	58

Bibliography

A Guide to the I Ching, K. Carol Anthony, Anthony Publishing Company, Stow, Massachusetts, 1988

An Anthology of I Ching, W. K. Chu & W. E. Sherril, Routledge & Kegan Paul, London, 1977

Authentic I-Ching: A New Translation with Commentary, Henry Wei, Newcastle Publications, North Hollywood, California, 1987

Change — Eight Lectures on the I Ching, Hellmut Wilhelm, translated by Cary F. Baynes, Princeton University Press, Princeton, New Jersey, 1973

Chi — A Neo-Taoist Approach to Life, R. G. H. Siu, MIT Press, Cambridge, Massachusetts, 1974

Doctors, Diviners and Magicians of Ancient China, Kenneth J. DeWoskin, Columbia University Press, New York, New York, 1983

Heaven, Earth, and Man, Hellmut Wilhelm, University of Washington Press, Seattle, Washington, 1977

I Ching, James Legge, edited by Raymond Van Over, New American Library, New York, New York, 1971

I Ching, Kerson & Rosemary Huang, Workman Publishing Company, Inc., New York, New York, 1985

I Ching, Sam Reifler, Bantam Books, New York, New York, 1991

I Ching: A New Interpretation for Modern Times, Sam Reifler, Bantam Books, New York, New York, 1985

I Ching: An Introduction to the Book of Changes, Willard Johnson, Shambhala Publications, Berkeley, California, 1969

I Ching, Book of Changes, James Legge, Bantam Books, New York, New York, 1980

I Ching Mandalas — A Program of Study for the Book of Changes, Thomas Cleary, Shambhala Publications, Inc., Boston, Massachusetts,

I Ching Numerology, Da Liu, Harper and Row, New York, New York, 1979

I Ching, the Book of Change, John Blofeld, Unwin Paperbacks, London, 1965

I Ching: The Book of Changes, Thomas Cleary, Shambhala Publications, Berkeley, California, 1992

I-Ching: The Hexagrams Revealed, Gary C. Melyan, C. E. Tuttle Co., London, 1976

I Ching Taoist Book of Days — Calendar Diary, Khigh Alx Dhiegh, Shambhala Publications, Berkeley, California, 1974

I Ching — The Tao of Organization, Cheng Yi, translated by Thomas Cleary, Shambhala Publications, Boston, Massachusetts, 1988

Images of Change: Painting on the I Ching, Terry Miller, Dutton Publishing Company, New York, New York, 1976

Introduction to the I Ching, Tom Riseman, Samuel Weiser, Inc., New York, New York, 1980

Lectures on the I Ching, Richard Wilhelm, Princeton University Press, Princeton,

New Jersey, 1979

Lectures on the I Ching — Constancy and Change, Hellmut Wilhelm, translated by Irene Eber, Princeton University Press, Princeton, New Jersey, 1979

"Mathematical Games: The Combinational Basis of the I Ching, The Chinese Book of Divination and Wisdom," Matthew Gardner, *Scientific American*, New York, New York, January, 1974

Moving with Change — A Woman's Re-integration of the I Ching, Rowena Patte, Routledge & Kegan Paul, London, 1986

On Divination and Synchronicity, Marie-Louise Von Franz, Inner City Books, Toronto, 1980

Pocket I-Ching, Gary C. Melyan & Chu Wen-kuang, C. E. Tuttle Co., London, 1988

Rediscover I Ching, Gregory Whincup, Doubleday, New York, New York, 1986

Researches on the I Ching, Julian K. Shchutskii, translated by William L. MacDonald *et al.*, Princeton University Press, Princeton, New Jersey, 1979

Science and Civilization in China, Vol. 2, Part 1, Joseph Needham, Cambridge University Press, Cambridge, 1979

Secrets of the I Ching, Joseph Murphy, Parker Publications, New York, New York, 1970

Self-development with the I Ching: A New Interpretation, Paul Sneddon, Avery Publishing, London, 1992

Simple I Ching, Ken Spaulding *et al.*, Vantage Books, New York, New York, 1978

Sung Dynasty Uses of the I Ching, Kidder Smith Jr. *et al.*, Princeton University Press, Princeton, New Jersey, 1990

Sychronicity: A Causal Connecting Principle, C. G. Jung, translated by R. F. C. Hull, Princeton University Press, Princeton, New Jersey, 1973

Synchronicity — The Bridge Between Matter and the Mind, F. David Peat, Bantam Books, New York, New York, 1988

T'ai Chi Ch'uan and I Ching, Da Liu, Harper and Row, New York, New York, 1978

The Astrology of the I Ching, W. K. Chu & W. E. Sherril, Routledge & Kegan Paul, London, 1976

The Book of Changes and the Unchanging Truth, Ni Hua-ching, Shrine of Eternal Breath of Tao, Los Angeles, California, 1983

The Book of Changes in the Western Tradition: A Selective Bibliography, Hellmut Wilhelm, University of Washington Press, Seattle, Washington, 1977

The Buddhist I Ching, Ou-i Chih-hsu, translated by Thomas Cleary, Shambhala Publications, Inc., Berkeley, California, 1987

The Complete I Ching for the Millions, Edward Albertson, Sherbourne Press, Los Angeles, California, 1969

The Eleventh Wing: An Exposition of the Dynamics of the I Ching for Now, Khigh Alx Dhiegh, Nash Publishing, Los Angeles, California, 1973

The Fortune-teller's I Ching, Ho Kwok Man, Martin Palmer & Joanne O'Brien, Ballantine Books, New York, New York, 1986

The I Ching: A Guide to Life's Turning Points, Brian B. Walker, St. Martin Press, New York, New York, 1992

The I Ching and Its Associations, Diana Ffarington Hook, Routledge and Kegan Paul, London, 1980

The I Ching and Mankind, Diana Ffarington Hook, Routledge and Kegan Paul, London, 1975

The I Ching and the Genetic Code — The Hidden Key to Life, Martin Schonberger, ASI Publishers, Inc., New York, New York, 1979

The I Ching and You, Diana Ffarington Hook, Routledge and Kegan Paul, London, 1973

The I Ching Coloring Book, Rita Aeor *et al.*, Doubleday, New York, New York, 1984

The I Ching of the Goddess, G. Barbara Walker, Harper & Row Publishers, Inc., New York, New York, 1986

The I Ching on Business and Decision Making, Guy Damian-Knight, Destiny Books, Rochester, Vermont, 1986

The I Ching or Book of Changes, Richard Wilhelm, translated by Cary Baynes, Princeton University Press, Princeton, New Jersey, 1979

The I Ching Workbook, R. L. Wing, Doubleday, New York, New York, 1979

The Illustrated I Ching, R. L. Wing, Dolphin Books/Doubleday & Company, Inc., Garden City, New York, 1982

The Inner Structure of the I Ching, Lama Anagarika Govinda, Rider and Company, London, 1981

The Man of Many Qualities: A Legacy of the I Ching, R. G. H.Siu, MIT Press, Cambridge, Massachusetts, 1968

The Nature of the I Ching, Its Usage and Interpretation, Charles Ponce, Award Books, New York, New York, 1970

The Oracle of Change, Alfred Douglas, Victor Gollanz, London, 1971

The Other Way: A Book of Meditation Experiences Based on the I Ching, K. Carol Anthony, Anthony Publishing Company, Stow, Massachusetts, 1990

The Philosophy of the I Ching, K. Carol Anthony, Anthony Publishing Company, Stow, Massachusetts, 1981

The Portable Dragon — The Western Man's Guide to the I Ching, R. G. H. Siu, MIT Press, Cambridge, Massachusetts, 1979

The Principles of Changes: Understanding the I Ching, Jung Young Lee, New York University Books, New York, 1971

The Taoist I Ching, Liu I-ming, translated by Thomas Cleary, Shambhala Publications, Boston, Massachusetts, 1986

Index

OTHER BOOKS ON CHINESE MEDICINE
AVAILABLE FROM BLUE POPPY PRESS
1775 Linden Ave, Boulder, CO 80304
For ordering 1-800-487-9296 PH. 303\447-8372 FAX 303\447-0740

A NEW AMERICAN ACUPUNCTURE by Mark Seem, ISBN 0-936185-44-9

ACUPUNCTURE AND MOXIBUSTION FORMULAS & TREATMENTS by Cheng Dan-an, ISBN 0-936185-68-6,

ACUTE ABDOMINAL SYNDROMES: Their Diagnosis & Treatment by Combined Chinese-Western Medicine by Alon Marcus, ISBN 0-936185-31-7

AGING & BLOOD STASIS: A New Approach to TCM Geriatrics by Yan De-xin, ISBN 0-936185-63-5

AIDS & ITS TREATMENT ACCORDING TO TRADITIONAL CHINESE MEDICINE by Huang Bing-shan, trans. by Fu-Di & Bob Flaws, ISBN 0-936185-28-7

ARISAL OF THE CLEAR: A Simple Guide to Healthy Eating, Bob Flaws, ISBN #-936185-27-9

THE BOOK OF JOOK: Chinese Medicinal Porridges, An Alternative to the Typical Western Breakfast by Bob Flaws, ISBN0-936185-60-0

CHINESE MEDICAL PALMISTRY: Your Health in Your Hand by Zong Xiao-fan & Gary Liscum, ISBN 0-936185-64-3

CHINESE MEDICINAL TEAS: Simple, Proven, Folk Formulas for Common Diseases by Zong & Liscum, ISBN 0-936185-76-7

CHINESE MEDICINAL WINES & ELIXIRS by B. Flaws, ISBN 0-936185-58-9

CHINESE PEDIATRIC MASSAGE THERAPY: A Parent's & Practitioner's Guide to Prevention & Treatment of Childhood Illness by Fan, ISBN 0-936185-54-6

CHINESE SELF-MASSAGE THE- RAPY: The Easy Way to Health by Fan Ya-li ISBN 0-936185-74-0

A COMPENDIUM OF TCM PATTERNS & TREATMENTS by Bob Flaws & Daniel Finney, ISBN 0-936185-70-8

CURING ARTHRITIS NATURALLY WITH CHINESE MEDICINE by Flaws & Frank, ISBN 0-936185-87-2

CURING HAY FEVER NATURALLY WITH CHINESE MEDICINE, by Bob Flaws, ISBN 0-936185-91-0

CURING INSOMNIA NATURALLY WITH CHINESE MEDICINE by Bob Flaws, ISBN 0-936185-86-4

CURING PMS NATURALLY WITH CHINESE MEDICINE by Bob Flaws, ISBN 0-936185-85-6

THE DAO OF INCREASING LONGEVITY AND CONSERVING ONE'S LIFE by Anna Lin & Bob Flaws, ISBN 0-936185-24-4

THE DIVINELY RESPONDING CLASSIC: A Translation of the Shen Ying Jing from Zhen Jiu Da Cheng, trans. by Yang & Liu ISBN 0-936185-55-4

DUI YAO: THE ART OF COMBINING CHINESE MEDICINALS by P. Sionneau. trans. by Bernard Côté. ISBN 0-936185-81-3

ENDOMETRIOSIS, INFERTILITY AND TCM: A Laywoman's Guide by Bob Flaws ISBN 0-936185-14-7

EXTRA TREATISES BASED ON INVESTIGATION & INQUIRY: A Translation of Zhu Dan-xi's Ge Zhi Yu Lun, by Yang & Duan, ISBN 0-936185-53-8

FIRE IN THE VALLEY: TCM Diagnosis & Treatment of Vaginal Diseases ISBN 0-936185-25-2

FLESHING OUT THE BONES: The Importance of Case Histories in Chin. Med. trans. by C. Chace. ISBN 0-936185-30-9

FU QING-ZHU'S GYNECOLOGY trans. by Yang and Liu, ISBN 0-936185-35-X

FULFILLING THE ESSENCE: A Handbook of Traditional & Contemporary Treatments for Female Infertility by Bob Flaws, ISBN 0-936185-48-1

GOLDEN NEEDLE WANG LE-TING: A 20th Century Master's Approach to Acupuncture by Yu Hui-chan and Han Fu-ru, trans. by Shuai Xue-zhong, ISBN 0-926185-78-3

A HANDBOOK OF TRADITIONAL CHINESE DERMATOLOGY by Liang, trans. by Zhang & Flaws, ISBN 0-936185-07-4

A HANDBOOK OF TRADITIONAL CHINESE GYNECOLOGY by Zhejiang College of TCM, trans. by Zhang Ting-liang, ISBN 0-936185-06-6 (4nd edit.)

A HANDBOOK OF MENSTRUAL DISEASES IN CHINESE MEDICINE by Bob Flaws ISBN 0-936185-82-1

A HANDBOOK of TCM PEDIATRICS by Bob Flaws, ISBN 0-936185-72-4

A HANDBOOK OF TCM UROLOGY & MALE SEXUAL DYSFUNCTION by Anna Lin, OMD, ISBN 0-936185-36-8

THE HEART & ESSENCE OF DAN-XI'S METHODS OF TREAT-MENT by Xu Dan-xi, trans. by Yang, ISBN 0-926185-49-X

THE HEART TRANSMISSION OF MEDICINE by Liu Yi-ren; translated by Yang Shou-zhong ISBN 0-936185-83-X

HIGHLIGHTS OF ANCIENT ACUPUNCTURE PRESCRIPTIONS trans. by Wolfe & Crescenz ISBN 0-936185-23-6

How to Have A HEALTHY PREGNANCY, HEALTHY BIRTH with Chinese Medicine by Wolfe, ISBN 0-936185-40-6

HOW TO WRITE A TCM HERBAL FORMULA: A Logical Methodology for the Formulation & Administration of Chinese Herbal Medicine in Decoction by Flaws, ISBN 0-936185-49-X

IMPERIAL SECRETS OF HEALTH & LONGEVITY by Flaws, ISBN 0-936185-51-1

KEEPING YOUR CHILD HEALTHY WITH CHINESE MEDICINE by Bob Flaws, ISBN 0-936185-71-6

Li Dong-yuan's TREATISE ON THE SPLEEN & STOMACH, A Translation of the Pi Wei Lun by Yang Shou-zhong & Li Jian-yong, ISBN 0-936185-41-4

LOW BACK PAIN: Care & Prevention with Chinese Medicine by Douglas Frank, ISBN 0-936185-66-X

MASTER HUA'S CLASSIC OF THE CENTRAL VISCERA by Hua Tuo, ISBN 0-936185-43-0

THE MEDICAL I CHING: Oracle of the Healer Within by Miki Shima, ISBN 0-936185-38-4

MENOPAUSE A Second Spring: Make a Smooth Transition with Chinese Medicine by Wolfe ISBN 0-936185-18-X

PAO ZHI: Introduction to Processing Chinese Medicinals to Enhance Their Therapeutic Effect, Philippe Sionneau, ISBN 0-936185-62-1

PATH OF PREGNANCY, VOL. I, Gestational Disorders by Bob Flaws, ISBN 0-936185-39-2 Vol. II, Postpartum Diseases by Bob Flaws. ISBN 0-936185-42-2

PRINCE WEN HUI'S COOK: Chinese Dietary Therapy by Bob Flaws & Honora Lee Wolfe, ISBN 0-912111-05-4

THE PULSE CLASSIC: A Translation of the Mai Jing by Wang Shu-he, trans. Yang Shou-zhong ISBN 0-936185-75-9

RECENT TCM RESEARCH FROM CHINA, trans. by Charles Chace & Bob Flaws, ISBN 0-936185-56-2

SEVENTY ESSENTIAL TCM FORMULAS FOR BEGINNERS by Bob Flaws, ISBN 0-936185-59-7

SHAOLIN SECRET FORMULAS for Treatment of External Injuries, by De Chan, ISBN 0-936185-08-2

STATEMENTS OF FACT IN TRADITIONAL CHINESE MEDICINE by Bob Flaws, ISBN 0-936185-52-X

STICKING TO THE POINT: A Rational Methodology for the Step by Step Formulation & Administration of an Acupuncture Treatment by Bob Flaws ISBN 0-936185-17-1

THE SYSTEMATIC CLASSIC OF ACUPUNCTURE & MOXIBUSTION (Jia Yi Jing) by Huang-fu Mi, trans. by Yang Shou-zhong and Charles Chace, ISBN 0-936185-29-5

THE TREATMENT OF DISEASE IN TCM, Vol I: Diseases of the Head & Face Including Mental/Emotional Disorders by Philippe Sionneau & Lü Gang, ISBN 0-936185-69-4

THE TREATMENT OF DISEASE IN TCM, Vol. II: Diseases of the Eyes, Ears, Nose, & Throat by Sionneau & Lü, ISBN 0-936185-69-4

THE TREATMENT OF DISEASE, VOL. III: Diseases of the Mouth, Lips, Tongue, Teeth & Gums, by Sionneau & Lü, ISBN 0-936185-79-1

THE TREATMENT OF DISEASE, VOL. IV: Diseases of the Upper & Lower Limbs, Neck, Shoulders & Back, by Sionneau & Lü, ISBN 0-936185-89-9

THE TREATMENT OF EXTERNAL DISEASES WITH ACUPUNCTURE & MOXIBUSTION by Yan Cui-lan and Zhu Yun-long, ISBN 0-936185-80-5